CATALOGUE 182   INCUNABULA

No. 7   Vincentius Bellovacensis (*reduced*)

INCUNABULA

WORKS FROM NINETY-EIGHT PRESSES IN
GERMANY, ITALY, SWITZERLAND, FRANCE,
HOLLAND, BELGIUM, SPAIN, & ENGLAND,
ARRANGED IN PROCTOR ORDER.

CATALOGUE 182

H. P. KRAUS, NEW YORK

H. P. KRAUS

16 EAST 46 STREET · NEW YORK, NY 10017
TELEPHONE: (212) 687-4808
FAX: (212) 983-4790

✢ GERMANY ✣

FROM THE GUTENBERG BIBLE

1 BIBLE. LATIN. O.T. – Liber Sapientiae (Wisdom of Solomon).
Chapter XIII:14–XV:18.

[Mainz, Johann Gutenberg?, 1454–55]

Folio (390 × 288 mm.). Gothic type. 42 lines. 2 cols. 1 f. (some light foxing).
2 large initials, chapter numbers and headlines supplied in red and blue;
capitals touched in red. Dark blue crushed morocco (spine rubbed). Book‑
plate of Wm. R. Smith.

An original leaf (vol. II, f. 22) from the Gutenberg Bible (Zouche copy,
broken up by Gabriel Wells). Bound with it is A. E. Newton's essay *A Noble
Fragment* (1921).

WITH BOTH THE 1465 AND 1466 COLOPHONS

2 CICERO, MARCUS TULLIUS. Officiorum liber [*and*] Paradoxa
[stoicorum]. (*With:*) HORATIUS FLACCUS, QUINTUS.
Manlio Torquato.

Mainz, Johann Fust and Peter [Schoffer], 4 February 1466

Large 8vo (226 × 161 mm.). Gothic type, with a few words of Greek. 28
lines. [88] ff. (last leaf hinged; last 5 ff. with few worm‑punctures), plus ff. 1
and 87 (colophon leaf) from the 1465 edition bound in at the end. With a
large illuminated initial supplied in blue and gold, and with a three‑sided
illuminated border from a vellum manuscript laid on the first page; headings
printed in red; rules in pale red throughout. A few neat contemporary mar‑
ginalia. Late 18th‑century English maroon morocco, with rich gilt floral and
pointillé tooling within geometrical strapwork compartments, gilt back,
g.e.; in a morocco‑backed drop‑case. From the library of Sir George Shuck‑
burgh, with his bookplate.

A splendid example of the art of typography in its infancy, and the last to bear the name of Fust as printer. This is the second book to have Greek type, it being preceded by the edition of the same work in the previous year. The last leaf is from that printing and therefore bears the first example of printed Latin verse, the poem of Horace addressed to Manlius Torquatus. So far as can be determined from de Ricci's descriptions, no other copy contains such added leaves. Many copies, however, are composed of a mixture of leaves of both the 1465 and 1466 editions, the latter being a line-for-line reprint of the 1465 edition. As with the 1462 Bible, copies on paper are rarer than those on vellum.

GW 6922; H 5239; BMC I, 24; Goff C-576; Pell 3726; Pol 1076; IGI 2885; IDL 1246; de Ricci (M) 85; see Adams, "Cicero: De Officiis . . . Mainz, 1465, 1466" in *The Library*, ser. 4, V, pp. 43–46.

A SCHÖFFER FOLIO ON VELLUM IN ITS ORIGINAL BINDING

3   THOMAS AQUINAS. Summa theologica. Secunda pars, secundus liber.

Mainz, Peter Schöffer, 6 March 1467

Printed on vellum. Large folio (398 × 285 mm.). Gothic types. 59 lines. 2 cols. [258] ff., including 3 cancels (several natural vellum flaws, some with original patching or mending; occasional insignificant spotting). Fine 11-line initial P in red and blue with elaborate purple penwork infilling and extension down the whole inner margin, incorporating two grotesque profile heads; 5- or 6-line initials supplied alternately in red or blue, with red or purple infilling and extensions; 2-line initials and paragraph marks in alternating red and blue; 3-line calligraphic heading in red on f. 1; headlines and Quaestio numbers supplied in red; capitals touched in red throughout the last quire, the Index. Original blind-stamped Mainz binding of calf over wooden boards (expertly rebacked), bevelled edges, brass and leather clasps (leather renewed), brass catches; traces of a chain staple at top of lower cover. Paste-downs of printed vellum waste from Schöffer's printing shop, the back one being the cancelland of f. 175 of the present edition, and the front being a register leaf from the same printer's edition of Thomas Aquinas *In quarto sententiarum*, 1469. In a half-morocco drop-box. From the library of Estelle Doheny, with her leather bookplate.

The earliest dated edition of any portion of this monumental work by one of the greatest mediaeval philosophers and theologians. This is the second edition of the Second Part of the *Summa*, following an undated edition of the same portion by Johann Mentelin.

Incipit secunda secunde doctoris sancti tho̅
de aquino. Questio prima de fide et
eius obiecto quod est veritas prima.

Post comune con-
sideracoem de
virtutibz et vi-
ciis. et aliis ad
materia morale
puñctibz. necce
est considerare sin-
gula in speciali.
Sermones eni
morales vniuer-
sales minus sut
vtiles. eo q̈ acciones in pticularibz sunt. Potest
aute aliquid inspeciali considerari circa moralia du-
pliciter. vno mo ex pte materie ipius moralis.
puta cu considatur de hac virtute. vel h̅ vicio. Alio
mo quatu ad speciales status hoim. puta cu cohi-
beratur de subditis i platis. de actiuis i cōteplatis.
vel quibusqz aliis differetiis hoim. Primo g̅
considerabimus spealiter de hiis q̈ puñet ad omes
hoim status. Scdo vero spealiter de hiis q̈ pti-
net ad determinatos status. Est aut considerans
du circa pmu. q̈ si seorsu determinaremus de virtutibz comis. viciis i pceptis. oporteret ide mul-
toties dice. qui eni sufficieter vult tractare de hoc
pcepto. no mechaberis. necce est inquire de adul-
terio. q̈ est quoddam pcem cuius etia cognitio de-
pendet ex cognicone opposite virtutis. Erit g̅ spe-
dichor i expeditior consideracois via. si simul sub
eode tractatu consideraco pcedit de virtute i dono
sibi correspondete i viciis oppositis. et pceptis
affirmatis vel negatis. Erit aute h̅ consideracois
modus conuemes ipis viciis h̅m ppria spez. Oste-
su est enim s̅ q̈ vicia i pcca diuersificatur specie.
h̅m materia vel obiectu. non aute h̅m alias dras
pccoru. puta cordis oris i opis. vel h̅m infirmi-
tate. ignorātia i malicia. et alias hmoi dras. Est
aute eade materia circa qua et virtus recte opat̅.
et vicia opposita a rectitudine recedut. Sic g̅ to
materia morali ad consideracoem virtutu reducta.
omes virtutes sut vlterius reducede ad septe. q̈z
tres sut theologice de auibz p̅mo ost̅ . . . .

Vellum copies are much rarer than paper; the only other American repository for a vellum copy is the Huntington Library. Three variant settings of the colophon are known and this copy corresponds to Hain and BMC.

The binding is from Kyriss 160, unlocalized, but a shop that did many bindings for Schöffer. Vera Sack has complied a list of bindings identified as being from this shop, including copies of this edition of Thomas Aquinas in the Stadtbibliothek Augsburg, Stadt-und Universitätsbibliothek Frankfurt am Main, and the Germanisches Nationalmuseum Nuremberg. The latter two copies also have Schöffer vellum waste. The present binding has the typical intersecting vertical, horizontal, and diagonal blind-stamped lines, with single stamps of a spread eagle, a rose, and a formalized lily. Both covers are almost identical except that the upper one bears two lettered stamps "Ihesus maria", one of which is upside down.

This copy has three cancels (ff. 3, 7, and 9 in quire 18) that are not mentioned in any other collation, vellum or paper, and we do not know if they are unique to this copy. The Pierpont Morgan Library's paper copy does not have them, but has the same setting on f. 175 as the waste copy used for a paste-down here.

A beautiful, wide-margined copy of an important incunabulum, printed in the same type as the 1459 Durandus, but with the rounded lower-case 'h' appearing for the first time.

H 1459; BMC I, 24; Goff T-209; Pell 1049; BNIC T-175; IGI 9588; IDL 4402; Van Praet I, 398; Oates 30; Kyriss 160, pl. 321–322; Sack, "Über Verlegereinbände Peter Schöffers", *AGB*, XIII (1973).

THE FIRST ACCOUNT OF A TRIP TO THE HOLY LAND
THE EARLIEST BOOK WITH FOLDING PLATES
THE FIRST TRAVEL BOOK WITH AUTHENTIC VIEWS

4 BREYDENBACH, BERNHARD VON. Peregrinatio in Terram sanctam.

Mainz, Erhard Reuwich, 11 February 1486

Folio (308 × 221 mm.). Gothic types. Variable number of lines. [147] of [148] ff. (lacking final blank, ff. 7 and 12 supplied from another copy;) plus 16 fold-out sheets (some folds expertly strengthened). 7 woodcuts of city views (several on multiple blocks); 1 full-page armorial cut; 9 cuts of Near Eastern people, animals and buildings; 6 cuts of alphabets; 2 woodcut initials and printer's device. Antique blind-stamped calf over wooden boards, with old brass center- and corner-pieces, and clasps and catches (stain from a chaining-staple visible at top verso of last leaf). In a felt-lined drop-case. Contemporary marginalia in two hands. From the library of Estelle Doheny, with her leather bookplate.

A large copy of the first edition of this celebrated account of a pilgrimage to Jerusalem and the monastery of St. Catherine on Mt. Sinai in 1483-84. Its

beth	zoy	waff	he	dolath	gomal	Beth	aleph
ↄↄ	J	O	O)	Q.	◁	◠	)ↄ

bree	zemoat	Nun	Mym·	lameth	kaph	Jod	theth
ℓ	﹏	⊢	⋈	⧵	⅄	ↄ	8

∞·	o	i	e	a	thaf ſyn	res·	koph	zsade	ffe
ꝝ	P	k	ℓ	Ʒ	6	ġ	℗	J	ↄ

4 Breydenbach

superb illustrations (in the opinion of William Morris "the best executed illus-trations in any mediaeval book") are by the artist Erhard Reuwich of Utrecht who accompanied Breydenbach, Dean of Mainz Cathedral, and several noble-men on the journey, and whom some scholars have thought may be identified with the "Hausbuchmeister." These wonderful woodcut views of Venice (on four sheets, i.e. over five feet long), Jerusalem (on three sheets), Candia (on two sheets), as well as those of Corfu, Modon, Parenza and Rhodes, are notable as archaeological records as well as outstanding examples of German woodcut art. The cuts of people in costume show Greeks, Copts, Turks, Armenians, etc. These woodcuts were subsequently used in the vernacular language editions which followed. The frontispiece is the first woodcut in which cross-hatching occurs.

Reuwich names himself as printer in the colophon, but because the types are Schöffer's the book has often been attributed to his shop; however, the general aspects of layout and composition do not accord with Schöffer's usual practices. For example, the widely differing lengths of text-pages imply inexpertly estimated copy, whereas Schöffer's texts are always a miracle of careful fitting.

Breydenbach (d. 1497), travelled to the Holy Land together with a young nobleman, Count Johann von Solms, who died during the voyage, and the knight Philip von Bicken. They left from Venice, went to Jerusalem, to St. Catherine's on Sinai, then to Alexandria, returning from there to Venice. In-cluded in the narrative are some remedies for sea-sickness, an Arabic-German vocabulary, remarks on the recent Turkish victories at Constantinople, and many descriptions of local costume and customs.

A fine copy of an essential volume in any collection of early illustrated books. Complete copies are very rarely met with on the market.

GW 5075; HC 3956; BMC I, 43; Goff B-1189; Pell 2929, Pol 894; IGI 2055; IDL 1024; Schramm XV, pp. 5, 7, ill. 1–24; Fairfax Murray 92; Schäfer 84; Schreiber 3628; Doheny I, 8; Davies, *Breydenbach*, 1.

4 Breydenbach

5   [GRUNBACH, JOHANN] LICHTENBERGER, JOHANN.
Prenosticatio Latina Anno lxxxviii ad magna[m] co[n]iunctione[m] Sa⸗
turni & Iovis q[ue] fuit a[n]no lxxxiiii ac eclipsim solis a[n]ni sequentis.
scz. xxxv co[n]fecta ac nu[n]c de novo eme[n]data.

Mainz, [Jacob Meydenbach], 8 June 1492

4to (258 × 193 mm.). [72] pp. (a few scattered wormholes). With 43 wood⸗
cuts of varying size, averaging c. 135 × 150 mm.; 2 large initials in a twisted
rope pattern, with flowers and another large woodcut initial. 16th⸗century
vellum, stamped in gold (now darkened) with two narrow borders of styl⸗
ized leaves with central medallions of delicate arabesque work. Ms. exlibris
at top of title of P. Schiller, of the Servite monastery at Vienna; book⸗label
of Paul Harth.

    Second Latin edition, with the same cuts as the first. The woodcuts have a
dramatic impact, employing bold black lines to compose strong, vigorous fig⸗
ures. The opening cut is a full⸗page illustration showing Ptolemy, Aristotle, a
Sibyl (Cumaean), St. Brigida and Reinhard the Lollard, all receiving inspiration
from heaven. The next cut depicts the author kneeling before God. Other illus⸗
trations refer to the predictions - the birth of a new prophet, the church threat⸗
ened with new perils, uprising in the Netherlands, etc. One amusing cut shows

the application of sumptuary laws – long hair is being shorn and long pointed toes cut off shoes, while a bonfire burns up playing-cards, dice and chessboards.

The first part of the book deals with the church, the second with the Holy Roman Empire, and the third with the people and private life; a section at the end makes predictions for well into the next century. It is based especially upon the conjunction of Saturn and Jupiter in 1484 in Scorpio, of Mars and Saturn in the same sign in the following year, and of an eclipse of the sun in 1485. A feature of Lichtenberger's prognostications is that they are obviously intended primarily for the Holy Roman Empire and its adjoining states such as Hungary, Bohemia, etc. It nevertheless enjoyed great popularity in Italy and many Italian editions were issued. Political and religious opinions are also expressed in the work, such as the justification of monarchy, and the king of the Romans in particular, and the perverseness of the Jews in not accepting Christianity.

The book is important for its outline illustrations of which Domenico Fava traces the influence on Italian woodcut books in an article in *Gutenberg Jahrbuch* (1930), pp. 126-148.

H 10082; Goff L-205; Klebs 606.6; Schreiber 4500; Schramm XV 1099-1141; Fairfax Murray 239; Muther 643.

THE FIRST EDITION OF VALERIUS MAXIMUS

6   VALERIUS MAXIMUS. Facta et Dicta Memorabilia.

[Strassburg, Johann Mentelin, not after 1470]

Folio (260 × 182 mm.). Gothic type. 34 lines. 159 ff. (of 160, final blank not present). Initials supplied in red. Brown calf, blind-ruled and -stamped, brass clasps, in 15th-century style.

A fine copy of the editio princeps, and one of the few classical authors to be first issued by a German press. The work is a collection of anecdotes drawn from Roman and Greek history, classified by subject, intended as a stock of illustrative examples to be incorporated into orations or rhetorical exercises, and used as a school-book. Though much of the material is taken from Cicero and Livy, it includes some stories from the author's own time (first century) and is thus an important original source for the reign of Tiberius. It is the first extant example of the unctuous melodramatic style of later Latin prose, and its long career as one of the most used textbooks of the Middle Ages and Renaissance was responsible for the spread and longevity of this style, both in Latin and the vernacular languages. At least twenty-three editions appeared before 1501 and Schweiger lists one hundred editions published between 1501 and 1600. There have, of course, also been numerous translations.

F. 132, which is reset in some copies, is here present in the first state.

Hain 15773; BMC I, 55; Goff V-22; IGI 10054; IDL 4553; Schorbach, *Mentelin*, 17.

7   VINCENTIUS BELLOVACENSIS. Speculu[m] doctri[n]ale.
       [Strassburg, The R-Printer (Adolf Rusch), before 11 February 1478]

Large thick folio (460 × 337 mm.). Semi-gothic type. 67–68 lines. 2 cols. [403] of 404 ff., first blank used as paste-down (lacking final blank; insignificant light browning on a few leaves, one or two minor marginal tears and some slight worming on first blank and first text leaf, affecting a few letters). Some old ms. quiring. Initials supplied in red, some with extenders, paragraph marks and capitals touched in red; space for large opening initial left blank. Occasional rubricator's marginalia. Beautiful original South German (Augsburg?) monastic binding of blind-stamped pigskin over bevelled wooden boards (a few minor worm-punctures and a crack in the pigskin about 10 cm. long in lower cover), panelled with double and triple rules, and with 9 different single stamps; 5 large chiselled brass bosses on each side, with clasps (leather renewed) and brass catches. Ms. exlibris of the monastery of St. Mang at Füssen in top margin of first leaf, with their 15th-century paper title-label and separate paper shelf-mark on front cover; bookplate of the Starkenstein family of Switzerland.

Magnificent copy of the first edition of Vincent of Beauvais' *Speculum doctrinale*, the rarest of his four *Specula* (*Speculum naturale, Speculum historiale,* and *Speculum morale* being the others), the huge compendium of mediaeval knowledge written in the thirteenth century. The present work consists of seventeen books and is a summary of all the scholastic knowledge of the age. It treats of grammar, logic, rhetoric, and poetry; various aspects of agriculture; canonical, civil and criminal law; the mechanic arts, medicine, mathematics, natural history, and the education and duties of a prince. Also included, after the first book, is a long Latin vocabulary.

Two variant settings are known (see Polain), the present one is that listed first by Polain and Goff, but no priority has been established and the printing of the other issue of some quires was no doubt due to damage in the printing shop. The date of 11 February 1478 occurs in a letter from the City Council of Lübeck to that of Strassburg regarding the loan of a manuscript of the present work to either Adolph Rusch or Johann Mentelin for printing. Mentelin did not print this work and Rusch's edition thereby acquires a terminus ante quem. Rusch, of course, was Mentelin's son-in-law.

This splendid binding bears tools typically found in several southern German workshops. There is a "Maria hilf uns" which Kyriss does not list, a palmetto, a large rose in a square, two small circular flowers of different sizes, two sizes of fleur de lys in a lozenge, a pineapple, a leafy spray, and a small oblong stamp of two circular flowers. The workshop whose tools these most closely resemble appears to be Kyriss 90, Augsburg.

[Facsimile of an early printed Latin text in two columns — Vincentius Bellovacensis]

No. 7 Vincentius Bellovacensis (*reduced*)

There are extensive early ms. notes on the inside front cover and the recto of the first blank, but these have been rendered difficult to read by some glue or paste partially adhering from the first blank's use as a paste-down.

A remarkably clean, crisp uncut copy on thick paper in its original binding.

C 6242; BMC I, 65 (second variant); Goff V-278; Pol 3938; IDL 4644; Osler 137A; Klebs 1037.1 (note); Dziatzko, "Der Drucker mit dem bizarren R" in *S.B.A.*, Part 17 (1904), pp. 13–24; Kyriss no. 90, pl. 183.

8   GERSON, JOANNES. Collectoriu[m] sup[er] magnificat.

[Strassburg, Heinrich Eggestein], 1473

Small folio (284 × 215 mm.). Semi-gothic type. 38 lines. [168] ff. including
final blank leaf (without the 2 conjugate ff. of instructions to rubricator and
binder, missing in almost all copies, but containing 2 contemporary blank
ff.). Printed musical notation (f. 4), spaces left for capitals. Contemporary
German blind-tooled pigskin over bevelled oak boards, the covers in a panel
design, the central panel with a floral diaper with large rosette tools, the
broad inner frame with alternating impressions of a palmetto and a "maria"
scroll, the narrow outermost frame with a lattice roll, spine with two raised
bands and repeated impressions of the palmetto tool, original clasps and
catches, ms. title-label on spine and on upper cover (the latter erased, stain
on back cover). From the libraries of the Benedictine Abbey of Ottobeuren,
with its 18th-century ms. exlibris on first leaf (partly erased but visible in
ultraviolet light); of the Allan Library, London, with its purple stamp on
first and last leaf; of the London Library, with its purple stamp and release
stamp on first and last leaf, and an embossed stamp on a few leaves (its sale,
Sotheby, 14 June 1966, lot 12); and of Eric Sexton, with his sticker and
leather bookplate (his sale, Christie NY, 8 April 1981, lot 56).

First edition of Gerson's *Collectorium*, the first attempt, apart from liturgies, to
print musical notation with movable type, in a contemporary German binding,
from the famous abbey of Saints Alexander and Theodore in Ottobeuren. Formerly attributed to the press of Conrad Fyner at Esslingen (see BMC II, 512),
Victor Scholderer showed in 1950 that the type B used in the present work was
the font of Fyner's mentor Eggestein in Strasbourg.

Jean Charlier of Gerson (d. 1429), chancellor of the University of Paris,
wrote this work as a mystical elaboration of the ideas conveyed in the words of
the *Magnificat*. He used the music in a discussion touching spiritual harmony. The
five principal notes of the scale are printed as identical squares and shown well
spaced descending regularly (f. 4). The lines of the staff are not printed, but left
to be ruled by hand. Some copies of the book have the clef printed from letter
type as here where a letter "f" appears at the left.

BMC and other modern bibliographies call for a double-leaf with instructions to the rubricator and binder at the beginning of the book, although the BL
copy and almost all other copies known lack these leaves. Whether these 2 ff. are
to be considered part of the book is questionable given their content. It is interesting to note that our copy has a conjugate of two contemporary blank leaves at
the beginning which once surrounded the first quire. These leaves bear the crown

with diadem watermark (Briquet 4890: Augsburg?, Innsbruck, 1474). This issue has "ope" as the last word on f. 70 [g10].

The present copy was listed in the 18th century by the librarian of the abbey, Father Michael Reichbeck (d. 1755, see Hubay, *Ottobeuren* p. 266) but has since remained untraced.

A beautiful, wide-margined copy in the well-preserved original binding.

H 7717; BMC II, 512; Goff G-199; I. Hubay, *Incunabula Augsburg* (1974), 880 (lacking rubrication ff.); I. Hubay, *Incunabula ... in der Benediktinerabtei Ottobeuren* (1970), p. 266; V. Sack, *Die Inkunabeln... Freiburg im Breisgau* (1985), 1544–1555 (one copy lacks rubrication ff., the other has them bound at the end, but lacks the final blank); V. Scholderer, "Notes on the Incunabula of Esslingen," *Gutenberg Jahrbuch*, 1950, pp. 167–171, reprinted in his *Fifty Essays*, 1962, pp. 224–228.

et ista notes Confozmacio ad quinqͥ notulas fol/fa/mi/re/ut/Quis quis aduertere diligenter voluerit᷈ inuemet qͣ ois meditacio falubris tam diumarum qͣ humanaᴣ fcienciarũ reduci poteſt ad quinqͣ verba quoᴣ quatuoz prima deũ refpiciunt fcᴣ magnificencia/munificécia ͥmi fericozdia/iuſticia/Qumtũ eſt hommi fpeciale videlicᴣ miferia Omne ſiqꝺ camicũ ſpũs ꝫ cozdis habet fozmari fcõm alterum quimqͣ ver᷈ boᴣ feu duoᴣ feu triũ feu ommũ fimul predictoᴣ Poffent fiᵽ omẽs cozdis et fpiritus affediones ad nũm deduci quimariũ que funt gaudiũ ſpes/cõpaffio/timoz/doloz/a applicando fingulũ verbũ lͣris meditacõis fingule p ozdinem hic pofitum voci fonantis affedõis Demum qniqͣ vocales ozdine nafali pofite notule ſit moicateſ cui voci lͣra fit accomo da edã p depſſionͤ et eleuacõs ad mſtar game nafaᵽ fol/fa/mi/re/ut/ Aut ponaᵽ ozdo nature vocaliũ deptis ꝫfonantiᵴ ut pᴣ in hac figura·

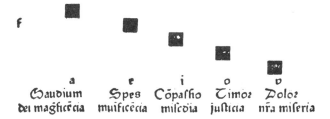

f

a e i o v
Gaudium Spes Cõpaffio Timoz Doloz
dei magͣficͤcia munificécia mifcõia iuſticia nͣra miferia

Nolumus aũt ut erſiſtimet aliquis gͣtia pͣs muſicoᴣ oim canticoᴣ valere ꝑtin⁹ efficaciter vt catͣt coz ꝫ ſpũs p affedũ fiᵽ ꝫ effedũ nõ fu erit huic arti de fe ꝺgnite facilime fupadditus pfertim in muſica fenſu ali fic ꝫ in pfalterio ꝫ cpthara·fic in chozo vocali fic in cozdis ꝫ ozgaͥ no Sed nec oportet nec erpedit fola pͣniũ fantaſia figurali vſari diu cius qͣ ducantur ad intelligencie puritatͤ fantaſmatiᵴ vel tranfcenfis ᵽ interim quantũ fas extiterit derelidis nec ideo putanda eſt pͣs ars in utilis vel fupuacua vel folũ fantaſialis qͣm pͣs eſt qͤ animale fcõm a· poſtolũ ꝫ omnis noſtra cognͣio intelledua fumit a fenſitia pricipiͥ que iuuatur dũ ozomata fibi fantaſmata pͣtatur ꝫ fub cõpendio hoc vnũ fidenter pollicemur qͣ pͣs ars tanqͣ in vtero nature fõmata cui nulla eſt lingua barbara vel ignota bradicabilis erit ommibus et per omnes fine difcrecione ideomatum qui conuerti voluerint ad coz vbi tamquã in libro fcriptum eſt impreffum·ꝫ fignatum ꝫ notulatũ·licet obumbratum in multis pfcriptũ ternariũ Nam quis negauerit deũi

8 Gerson (*reduced*)

9 AUGUSTINUS (PSEUDO). [Manuale] Liber p[ro]locutionis . . . liber de meditatione.

[Strassburg, Printer of the Henricus Ariminensis, c. 1476]

Small folio (285 × 212 mm.). Gothic type. 30–34 lines. [14] ff. (first leaf and last blank page with light soiling; few marginal wormholes or punctures at top and bottom). Two initials by a contemporary hand on first page, 'Q' (5-line) and 'N' (4-line), illuminated in gold, silver (partly oxidized) and colors (somewhat rubbed), with marginal extensions almost to last line of text and halfway across; 5-line initial 'T' supplied in red. Paragraph marks, slashes, and capitals touched in red. Old vellum. Early ms. library exlibris (mostly inked over) on first leaf, of Bibliotheca Ninoviensis? (Ninove, in Belgium); from the collection of Walter Goldwater, with his bookplate.

First edition of the complete text as quoted by the Maurists in the best edition of works by or ascribed to Augustinus (Paris, 1679-1700; see Migne below) and the only incunabular one, of this popular devotional text.

The important Strassburg printing shop represented by the present work has so far remained unidentified. Its history is complicated by the fact that variant founts of its types were used simultaneously by several printers – for example, Heinrich Knoblochtzer, Georg Reyser, and Michael Greyff. It appears to have been active from the early to the late 1470's; the 1468 rubrication date in the University of Toronto's copy of Petrus Lombardus' *Sententiae* from this press is erroneous.

Copies are quite rare, there is none in BMC or in Polain.

H 2102; GW 2969; Goff A-1284 (this copy); Pell 1587; IDL 555; Ritter, *Cat. des Incunables Alsaciens*, no. 57; Migne XL, pp. 951-967.

10 VALLA, LAURENTIUS. De libero arbitrio et providencia divina . . .

[Strassburg, Georg Husner, c. 1475]

Small folio (284 × 202 mm.). Gothic type. 35 lines. [10] ff. (outer conjugate rehinged, first leaf stained in margins just touching headline, a few marginal worm-punctures not affecting text). Large initial supplied and capitals touched in red on first page. Sixteenth-century Italian printed leaf over boards.

First edition of this radical humanist tract on free will. Lorenzo Valla (c. 1406-57), Professor of Eloquence at Rome and one of the first exponents of modern methods of historical criticism, argues here against the philosophical possibility of reconciliation between the concepts of free will and divine predestination. A noted philologist whose *De elegantia linguae latinae* was long the standard work on humanist Latin, Valla achieved notoriety with his proof of the spuriousness of the *Donatio Constantini*, in which he bitterly attacked the temporal power of the papacy. Henceforward, Valla was suspiciously eyed by the Vatican for heresy throughout his career, and his writings deeply influenced Renaissance scholars and Reformers. Luther especially held him in high esteem.

No other copy of this incunabulum has appeared at auction in this century. Its printer, Georg Husner, was active in Strassburg both as printer and goldsmith from 1470 to 1506, and his gothic type is unusually striking in its elegant variations of thickness and roundness. The three-line title is set in particularly unusual and fantastic majuscules. An exceptionally wide-margined copy of a very scarce and interesting text.

H 15830; BMC I, 83; Goff V-70; Pell 11415; BNIC V-50.

IN THE ORIGINAL BINDING

11   [PSEUDO-] AUGUSTINUS. – AMBROSIUS MASSARIUS CORIOLANUS, *comm.*; TILMANN LIMPERGER, JAKOB FEDDERER, & JOHANN SCHERREŔ, *eds.* Canones iuxta regulam

Strassburg, Martin Schott, 1490

Small folio (286 × 200 mm.). Gothic type. 52 lines. 2 cols. [2], cxxxiii, 1 blank, [11] ff. (lacking the second blank; light damp-staining in upper portion of many leaves; insignificant marginal worming at beginning and towards end). 4 full-page woodcuts (one being a repeat), three of them with neat contemporary water-coloring, the repeat left (deliberately?) uncolored. Capital spaces, many with guide letters. Original blind-tooled pigskin over wooden boards, ms. paper labels on front cover and spine, clasps missing. From the monastery library of Altomünster, Bavaria, with its ms. exlibris, dated 1543, on the inside front cover. In cloth drop-case.

First edition of this beautiful early woodcut book. The cuts represent St. Augustine, to whom this text is attributed, standing in a landscape; on his throne with two friars kneeling; and seated in a landscape teaching kneeling friars.

The misprint on the title-page has been corrected with a printed slip pasted over the error, reading as variant 1 in GW.

This copy is in its well-preserved original binding, its rear paste-down dated "1493" in ms.

GW 2937; H 2076; BMC I, 95; Goff A-1229; Pell 1568; Pol 393; IGI I, 965; Schreiber 3392; Schramm XIX, 16; Ritter, *Hist. de l'imprimerie alsacienne*, pp. 73–74 (with illus.); Schmidt 9.

12   [PETRUS DE PALUDE.] Sermones Thesauri novi de tempore.

Strassburg, [Printer of the 1483 "Vitas patrum"], 1486

Small folio (295 × 205 mm.). Gothic type. 48 lines. 2 cols. [352] ff. including final blank (title leaf a little soiled, blank corner of f.y₃ torn), plus 2
vellum fly-leaves. Very handsome 12-line initial on the first page of text
supplied by the rubricator, in blue with white scrollwork, delicate infilling
of red and blue tracery, and red penwork extensions; 3- or 4-line Lombard
capitals supplied in red; capitals touched in red; neatly rubricated throughout. Contemporary, probably original binding of dark brown blind-stamped
calf over wooden boards (skilfully and unobtrusively rebacked; some minor
rubbing; clasps removed), double rules dividing the sides into panels, and
diagonal rules dividing the central panels into lozenges; in the various compartments are single stamps of winged lions in squares and small roses. From
the libraries of the Rouge-Cloître, an abbey near Brussels, with its ms. exlibris on second leaf; and of the Infirmerie Marie-Therèse, with its small oval
stamp on title.

Petrus de Palude was an influential French theologian and scholastic (c.
1280-1342). This is quite a rare edition of a work which enjoyed a particular
popularity in Strassburg. There were numerous editions by various Strassburg
printers, though there seems to be to us no compelling reason why that should be
so, and the work is not at all common in any edition.

This is a fine copy in very fresh condition, meticulously rubricated and in a
good 15th-century binding.

C 5413 (J. Prüss); Goff P-521 (2 copies, one of them in the trade); Pol 2967; not in BMC.

13   JORDANUS DE QUEDLINBURG. Opus Postillaru[m] et Sermo-
num de Tempore.

Strassburg, [Printer of the 1483 Jordanus de Quedlinburg], 1483

Folio (328 × 226 mm.). Gothic type. 53 lines. 2 cols. [234, 184] = [418] ff.,
including the 3 blanks (first and last leaves a little soiled, occasional insignificant foxing). Lombardic initials supplied in red, opening Prologue initial in larger size with infilling of penwork tracery in brown; paragraph
marks in red. 17th-century vellum binding employing original sewing and
cords; narrow double blind-stamped rules on sides, with bands of triple
rules on back; remnants of green silk ties. Ms. exlibris on front endleaf of
Gerda Schulz-Schaeffer, geb. Heine.

This volume is the foremost of a group of books to which no printer's name
has so far been attached, and which caused Proctor to assign the eponym "Printer
of the 1483 Jordanus de Quedlinburg" to all these books. The regular develop-

13   Jordanus de Quedlinburg (*reduced*)

ment of the text types, and the use of the same display types, together with choice of text and method of dating, all seem to suggest one person directing the press for its duration. However, the output of this press has generally been assigned to Georg Husner on the basis of an article by Voulliéme in the *Zentralblatt für Bibliothekswesen* for 1915. The total output of the press is put at one hundred editions by Scholderer, but since three of the books partially employed the types of another eponymous Strassburg press, the Printer of the Casus breves, and one had some quires in Husner types, Voulliéme believed he had found sufficient evidence to prove that the printer was Georg Husner. Scholderer, however, in an article on this printer in *Fifty Essays* points out that if it is accepted that Husner was the Printer of the Casus breves (as agreed by Proctor and Voulliéme), then it would hardly seem possible for him to have also owned the Jordanus press. The types of the Casus breves later reappear slightly altered in Husner's own work, but those of the Jordanus press, though similar, show constant deviations from boht the Casus breves group and Husner's. This would be expected if the presses had different owners, but if all the material belonged to Husner it would be much harder to account for. Also, all the Jordanus press books from 1485 (the press was active in 1481) on until the end of the century are dated with a saint's day in every case, whereas this method of dating is used only once by Husner, and that in a reprint of a Jordanus edition. Scholderer concludes that Husner may well have worked at the Jordanus press, but probably only as a foreman.

Jordanus of Quedlinburg was an Augustinian of the early fourteenth century. He was the author of various theological works including a life of St. Augustine and a history of his order.

This is a fine copy, handsomely rubricated, of a work from a press that is still a mystery in the history of early printing.

HC 9438; BMC I, 131; Goff J-477; BNCI J-304; Pol 2328; IGI 5381; Voulliéme, *Zentralblatt f. Biblw.* (1915), 32, p. 309ff; Scholderer, *Fifty Essays* (1966), pp. 240–43.

14   AUGUSTINUS, AURELIUS. Opuscula Plurima.

Strassburg, Martin Flach, 11 August, 1491

Folio (284 × 202 mm.). Gothic type. 49 lines. 2 cols. [6], 267 + 1 blank = [274] ff. (7 ff. with small repairs to margins, 3 ff. with some staining; some scattered wormholes towards the end, occasionally affecting a letter of text). Very fine initials supplied in red, many with elaborate penwork extensions; paragraph marks in red and headlines and folios underlined in red. Original blind-stamped brown leather over wooden boards (new endpapers); outer border of intertwined stylized lilies and inner border of braided strapwork; inside this is a border of single small knotwork stamps and tiny carnations around a central panel of curving stems with flower ornaments (top and bottom of spine restored, minor repairs to covers). On the title-leaf is the exlibris of J. Rumpfhan.

This edition contains all the shorter works of Augustinus, and has a biography of him by Posidonius at the end. A very nice copy with good margins.

The binding appears to be from a monastic house of Augsburg, probably that of Sts. Ulrich and Afra, as a very similar binding is recorded from that house.

GW 2868; HC 1950; BMC I, 151; Goff A-1221; IGI 1019; IDL 527; Schmidt 34; Kyriss II, 91, nos. 1, 3, 4, 5 and 9.

Rupertus dei et aplice sedis gra Epus Ratispon Palatinus Reni Dux Bauarie et Comes in sponheim.

15 Breviary, woodcut by Wohlgemuth (*reduced*)

Incipit psalterium et breuiarium scom
choz ecclesie Ratisponen. Dominicis
diebus ad matut].inuitatoriu. Regem
magnu dnm.venite adorem². ps. Venite.

Beat⁹ vir qui nó
abijt in consilio
impioru: τ in
via peccatorum
nó stetit:et in ca
thedra pestilen
tie non sedit .

Sed i lege dni
voluntas ei⁹:et
in lege ei⁹ meditabit die ac nocte. Et
erit tanq lignu qd plantatu² est secus
decursus aquaz:qd fructu suu dabit in
tpe suo. Et foliu ei⁹ nó defluet:et oia
qcunqz faciet prsperabunt. Nó sic im
pij nó sic: sed tanq puluis quem picit
ventus a facie terre. Ideo nó resurgut
impij in iudicio:neqz peccatores in con
silio iustoz. Quonia nouit dns viam
iustoz: τ iter impioz peribit. ps. dd.

Quare fremuerut gentes:et popu
li meditati sunt inania? Astite
runt reges terre:et principes conueneft
in vnu aduersus dnm τ aduersus xpm
eius. Disrumpamus vincula coz:et
piciam⁹ a nobis iugu ipsoz. Qui ha
bitat in celis irridebit eos:et dns sub
sannabit eos. Tunc loquet ad eos in
ira sua:et in furore suo coturbabit eos.
Ego aute costitutus sum rex ab eo su
per syon monte sanctuz eius: pdicans
pceptu eius. Dns dixit ad me:filius
me⁹ es tu:ego hodie genui te. Postu
la a me et dabo tibi gentes hereditatez
tua: et possessione tua terminos terre.
Reges eos in virga ferrea:tanq vas
figuli confringes eos. Et nunc reges
intelligite:erudimini q iudicatis terra
Seruite dno in timore:τ exultate ei cu
tremore. Apphendite disciplina. ne
quando irascat dns:τ pereatis de via
iusta. Cu exarserit in breui ira eius:
beati oes qui cofidunt in eo. ps. dd.

Domine quid multiplicati sunt q
tribulant me: multi insurgut ad
uersum me? Multi dicut anime mee:
nó est salus ipsi in deo eius. Tu aute
dne susceptor me⁹ es: gloria mea τ ex
altans caput meu. Voce mea ad dnm
clamaui:τ exaudiuit me de monte san
cto suo. Ego dormiui τ soporat⁹ sum
τ exurrexi:qm dns suscepit me. Non
timebo milia populi circudantis me:
exurge dne saluum me fac deus meus.
Qm tu percussisti oes aduersantes mi
hi sine causa: dentes peccatoru contri
uisti. Domini est salus: τ sup popu
lum tuu benedictio tua.   ps. dauid.

Cum inuocare exaudiuit me deus
iusticie mee: in tribulatione di
latasti michi. Miserere mei: et exaudi
oratóne mea. Filij hominu vsqzquo
graui corde: vt quid diligitis vanitate
et queritis mendaciu? Et scitote qm
mirificauit dns sanctu suu: dns exau
diet me dum clamauero ad eu. Irasci
mini et nolite peccare. q dicitis in coz
dibus vestris:τ in cubilib⁹ vestris co
pungimini. Sacrificate sacrificiu iusti
cie et sperate in dno. multi dicut: quis
ostedit nobis bona? Signatu est sup
nos lumen vultus tui dne:dedisti leti
cia in corde meo. A fructu frumeti vi
ni et olei sui:multiplicati sunt. In pa
ce in idipm: dormia et requiesca. Qm
tu dne singulariter i spe:costituisti me.

Verba mea aurib⁹ pcipe dne:intel
lige clamore meu. Intende vo
ci orationis mee:rex meus τ deus meus.
Qm ad te orabo dne:mane exaudies
voce mea. Mane astabo tibi et vide
bo:qm nó deus volens iniqtate tu es.
Neqz habitabit iuxta te malign⁹. ne
qz pmanebut iusti ante oculos tuos .
Odisti oes qui opant iniqtate:pdes
oes qui loquunt mendaciu. Virum
sanguinu τ dolosu abbominabit dns:
ego autem in multitudine misordie tue.
Introibo in domu tua:adorabo ad

15 BREVIARY (USE OF REGENSBURG). – RUPERT II (BISHOP OF
REGENSBURG), *ed.* Psalterium et breviariu[m] s[e]c[un]d[u]m cho[rum]
ecclesie Ratisponen[sis]. Pars Hiemalis [and] Pars Estivalis.

Bamberg, Johann Pfeyl, 10 October 1495

Large thick folio (360 × 265 mm.). Printed in red and black. Gothic type,
with numerous two- or one-line Lombard initials in red. 46 lines. 2 cols.
2 vols: [14], II-CCCCXXX (i.e. 15-438, foliation jumps from 380 to
400); [8], II-CCCXCV (i.e. 9-406), [10] ff. (few minor worm-punctures
in lower margins at beginning of both volumes, insignificant occasional
light damp-staining). Full-page woodcut in each volume by Michael Wohlgemuth and a full-page calendar woodcut with the Sun in the center attributed to Wilhelm Pleydenwurff. Two nine-line initials at the beginning of
the Psalter in each volume supplied by the rubricator in red and blue, with
purple pen-and-ink decoration extending into the margin. Superb original
binding of blind-stamped pigskin over wooden boards, with the arms of
Bishop Rupert stamped on each upper cover in black; the covers lettered
"Pars hyemalis" and "Pars estivalis" respectively; incised metal-and-leather
clasps with matching incised catches (vol. I with two small original repairs
to upper cover; bosses lacking on each volume). From the libraries of Duke
Rupert II, Bishop of Regensburg, with his supralibros on each volume; and
of the Cathedral at Regensburg, "Ad latus Praepositi seu dextrum" written
in each volume, with the date of 1606.

A magnificent copy of one of the rarest and most beautiful liturgical books,
bound for its editor and patron Rupert II, Duke of Bayern-Simmern and Bishop
of Regensburg (1492-1507). The text of the "Propria" in the "Winter" volume
is considered an important source for the history of the adoration of the Saints
in Bavaria.

The original binding is in the classic Nuremberg style, similar to Kyriss 112,
pl. 226. Vol. I, upper cover, has intersecting vertical and horizontal triple rules,
forming a central panel in which is a repeated vine-like motif forming ovals with
artichoke plants in their centers; on each side the "ragged staff" motif interspersed
with five-petalled roses; below are four single lozenge stamps with eagles, and four
similar with lions. At the top are the arms of the Bishop with the title lettered
above. The verso is divided by similar rules into panels; the side columns with
"ragged staff" and rose; in the central panel crossed by diagonal rules are single
larger lozenge stamps of lions and roses. Vol. II, upper cover, similar vine-like
motif but with a flowering plant in the center of each oval; sides similar to first
volume except that the roses are enclosed in circles and the pattern is carried along

15   Breviary, arms of Bishop of Regensburg on binding

the bottom of the central panel; below a row of single lozenge stamps of lilies; Bishop's arms and lettering at top of binding; verso with large lion lozenges and lilies. Stamping of very fine workmanship, in beautiful condition, except for minor defects noted above.

A splendid example of liturgical printing, with large full-page woodcuts in each volume representing Bishop Rupert kneeling with SS. Peter, Paul, and Wolfgang (Bishop of Regensburg in the tenth century). There is a ms. Index on the blank recto of f. 12 (vol. I), which has been inserted from another copy at an early stage.

The volumes were apparently kept in the cathedral at Regensburg on the Provost's side of the Altar, according to the inscription on the front endpaper, and received very little use, which accounts for their extremely fine condition.

Examples of Pfeyl's printing are of great rarity. He worked first with Heinrich Petzensteiner and Laurenz Sensenschmidt in Bamberg, and then alone. BMC lists only two works under his name, one in collaboration with the other two printers and one by himself. GW cites the BM as owning a copy of this Breviary, but it does not appear in BMC and is represented in the BM STC German by one volume only. There appear to be no complete sets in any institutional libraries outside Germany, and we have not been able to trace any complete copy at auction since World War II. This is one of the three copies cited in Goff, the other two being incomplete.

GW 5435; H 3886; Goff B-1177; Pell 2916 (incomplete); Schreiber 3621 & 3621a; Bohatta (Parma) 213 (incomplete); Bohatta (Lit. Bibl.) 370=374; Muther 666; Dodgson I, 248; Schottenloher, "Regensburg" in *Veröffentlichungen d. Gutenberg-Gesellschaft*, XIV–XIX (Mainz 1920), p. 81.

16 THOMAS AQUINAS (SAINT). Summa de Articul[is] fidei [et] Ecc⟨
[les]ie Sacrame[n]tis.

[Cologne, Ulrich Zel, c. 1470]

8 vo. (212 × 136 mm.). Gothic type. 27 lines. [30] pp., 1 blank f. First large
initial supplied in blue; some capitals touched in red. 19th⟨century leather⟨
backed marbled boards, by Johann Hoppen. From the libraries of the City
of Cologne, with its stamp in lower title margin; and of Joseph Nève
(Brussels).

One of three editions printed at Cologne by Ulrich Zel in his Type 1 (BMC
96). It is interesting to note that the capitals of only the inner 4 leaves of the first
quire are touched in red, the outer 4 leaves and the second quire being unrubri⟨
cated. This may offer some clue as to the division of labor among the rubricators.

H 1424; BMC III, 860; Goff T⟨274; Pell 1023; Pol 3740 (citing this copy); Voulliéme
1155; IGI 9526; IDL 4359; Ennen, *Katalog der Inkunabeln in der Stadt⟨Bibliothek zu Köln*,
no. 26 (citing this copy).

17 ANTONINUS FLORENTINUS. Summa confessionum. (*With*)
Chrysostomi sermo de poenitentia. (*Inc.*) [I]Ncipiu[n]t Rubrice super Trac⟨
tatu[m] de instructione seu directione simplicium confessorum.

[Cologne, Printer of the Historia S. Albani (Johann Guldenschaff?),
not after 1472]

Small 4to (208 × 142 mm.). Gothic type. 27 lines. [144] ff., including final
blank (small tear repaired in blank margin of first leaf). Large and small
initials, paragraph⟨marks, and underlines supplied in red, capitals touched
in red (occasional light offsetting of initials). French dark green morocco by
Honnelaître, with outer roll⟨stamp border of flowers and leafy scrolls, and
inner border of winged angel⟨heads, title stamped in gold on upper cover,
gold ornaments on lower cover and back, g.e., in morocco⟨edged slipcase.

A very attractive example of Cologne printing in the early 1470's. A copy
in the Staatsbibliothek, Munich, has a rubricator's date of 1472, giving us a
probable printing date.

Bradshaw was the first to separate a group of books from the work of Ulrich
Zel under the name of the Printer of the Historia S. Albani, by means of several
typographic distinctions. However, Geldner now assigns these books to the press
of Johann Guldenschaff, a former associate of Zel, whom he believes may have
started printing on his own in 1472.

The present work by the renowned archbishop of Florence was one of the
most popular works of the incunabular period and was considered an invaluable
adjunct to confessors.

GW 2085; C 489; BMC I, 215; Pell 820; IGI 618 (1 copy); Voull. (K) 128; Geldner I,
pp. 93–94; not in Goff.

18 LEO I (POPE). – JOHANNES ANDREAS, *ed.* Liber Sermonu[m].

[Cologne, Bartholomaeus de Unkel, c. 1475]

Small folio (268 × 196 mm.). Semi-gothic types. 38 lines. 2 cols. [125] ff. (of 126, lacking initial blank; first 4 ff. with some very minor thumbing and soiling). Lombardic initials supplied in red, with one larger initial at beginning of text; capitals touched and chapters underlined in red. 19th-century midnight blue morocco, tooled in blind, g.e., by Petit; silk marker. A few early marginalia. Inscription on lower margin of title noting that the book was from the library of the Society of the Reverend Fathers of Emmerich; incorporated into the library of the Franciscans of the Monastery of Mount Calvary at Elten, 19 March 1687; unidentified 19th-century bookplate by Lacoste aîné.

A fine wide-margined copy of this handsomely printed edition of the Sermons of Leo I (440-461), the only other Roman pontiff besides Gregory I to bear the surname The Great. "From his short and pithy *Sermones* many of the lessons now to be found in the Roman breviary have been taken." (Encyc. Brit.)

Bartholomaeus de Unkel was printing for only about ten years, beginning in 1475, and this is one of the early books employing the round "h".

H 7947.2; C 3543; BMC I, 241; Goff L-133; BNIC L-114; Pell 7124; IDL 2907; Voull (K) 739.

FIRST BOOK FROM THE PRESS OF BARTHOLOMAEUS DE UNKEL

19 LEO I, (SAINT AND POPE). – JOHANNES ANDRES, *ed.* Liber sermonu[m].

[Cologne, Bartholomaeus de Unkel, c. 1475]

Small folio (285 × 200 mm.). Gothic type. 38 lines. 2 cols. [124] ff. (of 126, lacking first and last blanks; tiny worm-punctures in lower margin of first quire; occasional light staining also in lower margin). Large opening 6-line initial in red and blue, other 3-line initials supplied in red, chapter headings underlined and capitals touched in red.
(*Bound with*:) GREGORIUS I (SAINT AND POPE). Homiliae super evangeliis. (*With*:) ORIGEN. Homiliae.

Cologne, Bartholomaeus de Unkel, [9 December] 1475

Gothic type. 38 lines. 2 cols. [134] ff. (last 2 quires slightly waterstained in outermost lower corner, also with a few tiny wormholes; last 7 ff. with rust-holes in upper margins caused by chain hasp). Initials supplied in red, some with extensions, chapter headings underlined and capitals touched in red.

obtinebim? fi ad illū ßo amo
re flagram? Qui uiuit ⁊c·

Scdm lucā

IN illo tpe Dixit ihs discipul'
suis Si qs venit ad me et non
odit pĩem suū et matrē et vx-
ozē et filios et fratres ⁊ sorores
adhuc aūt et aiaz suā. nõ potest meus esse discipul? Et qui
nõ baiulat cruce suā ⁊ vit pỗ
me nõ ꝑt esse meus discipul? ·
Et reliqua· Omelia beati gre-
gozij pape de eadē loẽ habita
ad ipl'm in basilica sci sebastia
mi mris in die natalis eius

SJ cõsiderem? frēs kmi
que ⁊ qnta sũt que no
bis ꝓmittuƮ in celis:
vilescūt aio oia que bñtur i ver
ris· Terrena nãqz substantia
eterne felicitati cõpata põdus
est nõ subsidiũ Tēpozalis vita
eterne vite ꝯpata mozs est po
tius dicēda q̃ vita Ipse eñ co
tidianꝰ defectus cozruptiois
qd est aliud q̃ quedã plixitas
moztis Que aūt lingua dixari
vel quis itellectus capē suffiat
illa supne etatis qnta sũt gau
dia: angeloz chozus interesfe
aū beatissimis spitibz glozie cõ
ditozis assiste: pñtez dei vultū
cerne mcircūscriptū lumē vide
nullo moztis metu affici: īcoz-
ruptiois ꝓpetue munē letari·
Sed ad hec audita mardescit
aīm? iãqz illuc cupit assisté v-
bi se sperat sine fine gaudere· ß

ad magna ꝓmia puenizi non
ꝑt· nisi ꝑ magnos laboresVñ
et paulus egregiꝰ ꝓdicatoz ðt
Nõ cozonabitur nisi qui legiti
me certauerit Delectet igiƮ men
tē magnitudo ꝓmioz ß nõ de-
terreat certamē laboz Vnde et
ad se venientibꝰ veritas ðt· Si
qs vult ad me et nõ odit patrē
suū et matrē et vxorē et filios
et fratres et sorores· adhuc āt
et aiaz suā nõ ꝑt meus esse di-
scipulus· Sed ꝑuinctari libet
quõ parētes et carnaliter pro
pinquos ꝗ̃pimur odisse q̃ iu
bemur et inimicos diligere·Et
certe de vxore veritas dicit Qo
deus iũxit homo non sepet Et
paulꝰ ait Vizi diligite vxozes
vestras sicut et xpc ecclesiam·
Ecce discipulus vxorem diligē
dam predicat aū magister dicat Qui vxorem nõ odit· non
potest meus esse discipul? Nũ
quid aliud iudex nũciat: aliud
ꝓco clamat: An simul et odisse possum? et diligere Sed si
vim ꝓcepti ꝑpendim? vtrūqz a
gere ꝑ discretionē valem? vt e-
os qui nobis carnis cognatio-
ne diũcti sũt· et quos ꝓximos
nouim? diligamus ⁊ quos ad
uersarios in via dei patimur o
diendo et fugiendo nesciamus:
Quasi eñ per odium diligitur
qui carnaliter sapiens dum ꝓ
ua nobis ingerit nõ auditur·
Vt autē dñs demonstraret hoc

Original dark brown calf over bevelled wooden boards (rebacked and with narrow portion of sides adjacent to back replaced, preserving original head/ and tailbands; holes at top of lower cover where chain once was); sides in diaper pattern with several single stamps, double/eagle in a square, tiny single eagle in a lozenge, tiny lion rampant in a lozenge, single and double fleurs de lys, both in lozenges, rosette in a circle, deer in a circle, hare in an oval, and "maria" and "ihesus" in rectangles; two brass and pigskin clasps. A quotation from Gregory's *Homiliae* on vellum pastedown in a contempo/rary hand.

The Gregorius is Bartholomaeus's first dated book, but it seems likely that the Leo I was printed at almost the same time. The two works in our copy were rubricated by the same hand and bound together in the original binding.

We have not been able to trace any of the nine different single binding stamps in Kyriss or Goldschmidt, and are therefore disposed to think that the binding either was done outside western Europe, or by some as yet unrecorded binder.

Leo I, who reigned as Pope from 440-461, was responsible for consolidating and advancing the influence of the Roman see to an enormous extent. His only extant works are sermons and letters.

His sermons are followed by the Homilies of Gregory the Great (reigned 590-604), considered the father of the mediaeval papacy. He showed great ability as an administrator. His *Homilies on the Gospels* were much drawn upon as lessons for the third Nocturn of the Breviary. Joined to these Homilies are those of Origen (c. 185-c. 254) one of the greatest scholars of Christian antiquity.

This volume is a fine example of the early printing of Bartholomaeus de Unkel, with the round 'h' which was later replaced somewhere between 1477 and 1481. He employed only one text type. There is some confusion over whether he printed for Quentell or whether Quentell took over his types c. 1485-86. Almost nothing is known of his life save that he came from the village of Unkel near Bonn.

A good, crisp partially uncut copy in its original binding.

Ad I: H 7947: C 3543; BMC I, 241; Goff L/133; IDL 2907; Voull (K) 709

Ad II: HC 7947; BMC I, 240-241; Goff G/419; Pell 5368; Pol 1708; IDL 2089; Voull (K) 507.

THE FIRST CATECHISM

20   GERSON, JOHANN. Conclusiones de diversis materiis moralib[us] . . . (*With:*) Opusculu[m] tripartitu[m] de preceptis decalogi, De confessione [et] de arte moriendi . . .

[Cologne, Bartholomaeus de Unkel, c. 1480]

Small 4to (210 × 140 mm.). Gothic type. 27 lines. 1 blank, [38], 2 blanks, [30], 1 blank ff. 2/5 line initials and numerous paragraph marks supplied in red, capitals touched in yellow, each page within faint brown rules, neat contemporary foliation and some headlines in brown ink. Dark green blind-tooled crushed morocco (spine faded), by G. Vignal. Ms. exlibris of the library of St. Sepulcre, Cambrai, at top of first text leaf; and unidentified bookplate with monogram C.P.

Two works on the nature and office of confession, intended as instructional treatises for the church and school, and so considered the first Catechism. Jean le Charlier de Gerson (1363-1429), Chancellor of Notre-Dame and sometimes dubbed the 'Father of Gallicanism,' was a prime mover in the Council of Constance, and in the drafting of the famous Four Articles of Constance. An adamant proponent of Church reform, he advocated the superiority of a general council including Doctors of Theology, of which he was one, over the Pope.

The handsome gothic type is that of Bartholomäus de Unkel, who was active in Cologne from 1475-84, and to whom the printing of both the great Cologne Bibles has been attributed. Copies of this edition are quite scarce, there being none in BM; Goff reports only one complete copy.

A beautifully clean and crisp copy, not in BMC.

H 7650 (lacking blanks); Goff G-208; Pell 5143; Pol 1601, citing only first work; IDL 1940; Voull (K) 463.

METRICAL VERSION OF PHYSIOLOGUS

21 THEOBALDUS (EPISCOPUS). Phisiologus de naturis duodecim animalium.
                                  [Cologne, Heinrich Quentell, 1495]

Small 4to. Gothic type. 44 lines (commentary). [14] ff. (some occasional light browning and spotting). Vellum.

This early printed edition of *Physiologus* is a metric version, with "interpretations" of twelve animals. These are the lion, eagle, serpent, ant, fox, elephant, stag, panther, turtle-dove, siren, whale, and spider. The work may be described as a symbolic Bestiary, in which the characteristics and properties of animals are accompanied by Christian allegories and instruction. Many versions of varying length are extent in Coptic, Syriac, Arabic and Armenian as well as Greek and Latin. It was enormously popular in the Middle Ages and its allegories are reflected in the animal sculptures of Gothic cathedrals and in the grotesque beasts in the margins of manuscripts.

The metrical text here is leaded and printed in a large size type, while the commentary is in a much smaller size. An attractive example of incunabular metrical printing.

Nothing is apparently known of the Theobaldus described at the beginning of the text as "magister, doctor & episcopus".

HC 15468; BMC I, 295; Goff T-140 (2 copies only); Klebs 956.8; Voull (K) 1131.

quondã forbũit ionã pphetã .qʒ illũ ad littus iterũ euomuit. hos aũt pifci
culos in ventre tenet. Cũc ibi. Si fit tẽpeftas. Autoʒ ponit fcõam natu
rã ceti dicẽs fic. qñ magna tẽpeftas ẽ in mari. fic qʒ procelle maris fundũ
cõmouet ʒ cõturbãt. ʒ aura ẽ calida. tũc cetus tollit fe de fundo ad aque
fũmitatẽ feu fupficiẽ. naute vidẽtes putãt hoc ẽ magnũ pmontoʒiũ. ʒ illʒ
lic cũ nauibʒ applicãt fe ʒ naues fuas cupiũt ibidẽ alligare ne pereãt tẽ
peftate. ʒ cõponũt ignẽ vt fe calefaciãt. ʒ cibaria coquãt. Cetus vero cũ
fentit caliditatẽ ignis fe immergit ʒ periclitãt naues ʒ ipe redũt ad loʒ
cũ fcʒ maris fundum vnde prius venit

Iribus eft ʒabulus quafi cetus coʒpoʒe magnus

Vt monftrant magni quos facit ille magi

Mentes cunctoʒum qui mutat vbiqʒ viroʒum

Efurit atqʒ fitit quofqʒ poteft perimit

Et modicos fidei trahit in dulcedine verbi

Ham fide firmos non trahit ille viros

In quo confidit quifquis et fpem fibi ponit

Ad ftiga qui rapitur qʒ male decipitur

Hec ẽ fcõa ps in q autoʒ ponit allegoriã de natura cet.ʒ dicit fic fi
cut cetus ẽ magnꝰ coʒpe. fic ʒabulꝰ .i. dyabolꝰ ẽ magnꝰ viribʒ. vt nigromã
tici affirmãt q ꝓrute dyabolica p arte magica magna ʒ mirabilia facere
vident. ʒ q vident etiã ẽ montes dyaboli in pelago. qʒ fuas deceptõnes
per vniuerfũ mũdũ diffũdũt. ʒ ficut cetꝰ in mari fert dulce flatũ quẽ per
os emittit pifces attrahit. nõ tñ magnos fʒ paruos. fic dyabolꝰ p fugge
ftionis fue dulcedine q ẽ in longa vita ʒ ꝯcupifcentia carnali attrahit fibi
paruos pifces. hoc ẽ hoies paruos ʒ modicos in fide ʒ bono ope. vel fi ca
pit talis nõ tenet eos fʒ euomit. ficut nec cetus tenuit quõdã ionã ppheta
Et ficut nauigãtes interdũ piclitãt imitãdo cetũ. fic hoies huiꝰ mũdi
in opibʒ imitãtes dyabolũ piclitabũtur qñ ipe immergit fe .i. qñ eʒ iuffu
diuino religabit in infernũ. fcʒ poft diẽ iudicij. ʒ tũc male decepti funt q ra
piitur ad ftiga .i. ad gehennã ignis.

De fyrene

Irenes funt monftra maris refonantia miris

Vocibus et modulis cantus facientia multis

Ad quas non caute veniunt fepiffime naute

Que faciunt fonitum nimia dulcedine vocum

Et modo naufragium modo dant moʒtale periculum

Ham qui viderunt has tales effe tulerunt

£ i

22 ALBERTANUS CAUSIDICUS BRIXIENSIS. Ars loque[n]di et
tacendi.

Cologne, [Heinrich Quentell], 1497

Small 4to (193 × 144 mm.). Gothic types. 35 lines. [12] ff., including final
blank (title-leaf slightly soiled and small tear repaired; small stain in fore
margin of f. 7). Initials, including 5-line opening 'Q', supplied in red, some
highlighted in silver; paragraph marks and headings underlined, and capitals touched, in red, many of these also highlighted with silver; title underlined and its capital 'A' stroked in red. Calf.

Jurist, philosopher, and magistrate of the thirteenth century, Albertano's
biographical details are scanty. While studying at Brescia he was entered in the
Corporation of "causidici", which meant that he was trained for public life. He
was certainly occupied with public affairs in his city of Brescia, traditionally a
Guelph stronghold. During the war against Frederick II he was imprisoned in
the Ghibelline city of Cremona where he wrote his first philosophical treatise.

According to the colophon, the present work on the art of knowing when to
speak and when to maintain silence, was written for the instruction of the author's
three sons. It was a fifteenth-century bestseller and appeared in many editions after
the mid 1470's.

A fine, crisp quarto from the second press of Heinrich Quentell. The last
leaf and the title in this copy have the impress of a title in blind from pressure
against standing type. Only two copies in Goff.

GW 563; HC 412; BMC I, 287; Goff A-209; Voull (K) 37; not in Pell or Pol.

EARLY PAGINATION

23 Fundamentum eterne felicitas . . .

Cologne, [Retro Minores (Martin von Werden?)] for Heinrich Quentell,
1498 [i.e., between 16 May 1498 and September 1499]

Small 8vo (135 × 99 mm.). Gothic type. 30 lines. 1 f., [4], 53, [5] pp. (4 ff.
with small marginal repairs). Large title woodcut, repeated on last page,
three 4- to 5-line initials supplied in blue, with red and yellow penwork
decoration extending into the margin, numerous 2-line initials supplied in
blue or red, rubricated throughout. Disbound, in cloth portfolio.

Rare first edition of this devotional book, containing comments in dialogue
form on the Articles of Faith, on the Lord's Prayer, and concerning mortal sins.
The woodcut depicts the Christ-child in the center, on the left St. Anne, and on
the right the Virgin Mary, and above the Holy Spirit represented by the dove. The
wood-engraving is masterfully executed, utilizing only a few strokes to offer a fine

representation of the holy scene. The block used is known to have been in the inventory of the Retro Minores workshop, and probably Quentell, as a busy publisher, had no time or inclination to have a new block cut for this work and simply ordered the woodcut from their workshop. This latter was founded and managed by Martin von Werden until 1504.

A very early and unusual example of incunabular printing with printed pagination "Pagina prima" to "Pagina LIII" in the middle of the upper margin. For the exact dating of this book see BMC I, 312.

Only one copy recorded in Goff (Huntington).

GW 10426; C 2601; BMC I, 312; Goff F-331; Voull. (K) 430; Schramm VIII, no. 491; about early pagination see: Paul Lehman, "Blätter, Seiten . . .", *Zentralblatt f. d. Bibl.wesen*, Jg. 53, p. 433.

23 Fundamentum eterne felicitas

Finit libellus diuina ecclesie sacrameta · que numero septem · et alia
qmplurima secum versans persalubria · p viris ecclesiasticis maxie
curatis · suboitop aiab3 puide habetib3 · cui titul3 i capite fulgidus ·
a Ginthero zeine de Reutlingen · artis huius ingeniose magistro ·
in vrbe augustensi impressus foeliciter. A partu virginis salutifero
anno currente Millesimo quadringentesimo sexagesimonono ·

Finit libellus diuina ecclesie sacrameta · que numero septem · et alia
qmplurima secum versans persalubria · p viris ecclesiasticis maxie
curatis · suboitop aiab3 puide habetib3 · cui titul3 i capite fulgidus ·
a Ginthero zeiner de Reutlingen · artis huius ingeniose magistro ·
in vrbe augustensi impressus feliciter. A partu virginis salutifero
anno currente Millesimo quadringentesimo sexagesimonono ·

24 Johannes de Auerbach, colophon and variant

ONE OF THE EARLIEST BOOKS PRINTED IN AUGSBURG
ORIGINAL VARIANT COLOPHON ATTACHED

24 AUERBACH, JOHANNES DE. Summa de auditione confessionis
et de sacramentis.   Augsburg, Günther Zainer, 1469

Small folio. Gothic type. 35 lines. [49] ff. (outermost edge of fore margin of
f. [1] remargined; part of lower margin of f. [16] very neatly patched;
washed). Dark green morocco, gilt, by Frieda Thiersch; in marbled board
morocco-edged slipcase. From the library of the Benedictine abbey at Wesso-
brunn, Bavaria, with its 18th-century bookplate; from the University Library at Landshut, with its library stamp and release stamp; and from the
library of Estelle Doheny, with her leather booklabel.

The second or third book printed in Augsburg, preceded only by Zainer's
Meditationes vitae Christi, 12 March 1468, and perhaps by the *Catholicon*, 30 April
1469. Laid in at the back of this copy is a trimmed sheet, probably printer's waste,
of the final leaf, f. [49]. This shows an earlier state of the colophon with (line 1)
an upside-down i in "alia"; (line 4) "zeine" for "zeiner"; (line 5) "foeliciter" for
"feliciter." GW notes the variant for "zeiner", and BMC notes also "foeliciter",
but neither records the upside-down "i".

The author was a priest in the diocese of Bamberg (fl. 1440's) and this work
was explicitly imposed for priestly reading in the synodal statutes of Brixen, 1449
and 1453, the latter being presided over by Nicholas of Cusa.

A beautiful wide-margined copy of a very early Zainer printing. An outstanding piece of early typography, and of particular interest for its variant colophon leaf.

GW 2852; H 2124; BMC II, 315; Goff A-1381; Pell 1599; Pol 431; IDL 478; Doheny
II, 9.

Ucio cecilio· Metello quinto fabio maximo feruiliano confu
libus· inter cetera prodigia androgenus rome vifus· iuffu
auruspicum in mare est merfus·Sed nichil impie expiationis pro
curatio profecit· ¶Nam tanta fubito peftilentia exorta est·ut mi
niftri quoq̃ faciendorum funerum primum non fufficerent· deinde
non effent·ita ut etiam magne domus vacue viuis·plene mortuis
remanerent·largiffime introrfum hereditates·et nulli penitus here
des· Deniq̃ iam non folum in vrbe viuendi· fed etiam appropin
quandi ad vrbem negabatur facultas·¶Tam feui per totam vrbem
tabefcentium fub tectis et in ftratis fuis cadauerum putores exala
bant·Expiatio illa crudelis·et viam mortibus hominum morte ho
minis inftruens· tandem romanis inter miferias fuas erubefcenti
bus qm̃ mifera et vana effet innotuit· Ante enim fuffragium pre
ueniende cladis est habita·et fic peftilentia confecuta est· Que tamẽ
fine ollis facrificiorum fatiffactionibus tantummodo fecundum
menfuram archani iudicij expleta correptione fedata est· quam fi
artifices illi circumuentionum aruspices fub ipfa ut affolent decli
natione morborum forte celebraffent· proculdubio fibi· dijs et riti
bus fuis·reducte fanitatis gloriam vendicaffent· ¶Ita mifera et
facrilega & male religiofa ciuitas a mendacijs quibus liberari nõ
poterat ludebatur· Capitulum·ix·/

Igitur fabius conful contra lufitanos et·Veriatum dimicãs
bocciam oppidum quod Veriatus obfidebat·depulfis hoftib̃
liberauit·et in deditionem cum plurimis alijs caftellis recepit· ¶
¶Fecit facinus etiam vltimis barbaris fcithie non dicam romane
fidei et moderationi execrabile·Quingentis enim principibus eorũ
quos focietate inuitatos deditionis iure fufceperat·manus prefcidit
¶Pompeius fequentis anni conful fines numantiorum ingreffus
accepta maxima clade difceffit·non folum exercitu pene omni profli
gato· verum etiam plurimis nobilium qui ei milicie aderant inter
emptis· ¶Veriatus cum poft quatuordecim annos romanos du
ces et exercatus protriuiffet infidijs fuorum interfectus est·in hoc fo
lo romanis circa cũ fortiter agentibus cp percuffores eius indignos

G S 1413 S.herding
Ø

25   Paulus Orosius, with rubricator's signature

25   OROSIUS, PAULUS. [Historiae adversus Paganos.]

Augsburg, Johannes Schüssler, "circiter" 7 June 1471

Folio (308 × 212 mm.). Gothic type. 35 lines. [130] ff. (of 133, lacking last 3 blanks; 3 ff. towards the end with faint waterstaining on outer fore-margin; small repair in upper blank margin of f. [113]), a few leaves uncut. Paragraph marks and initials of varying size supplied in red, the largest (6- or 7-line) with pen infilling in red and black; capitals touched, and some words underlined, in red. The rubricator, Georgius Sparsguet, has signed his name in full, with date of 1473, on f. [32]; on 6 other leaves he has signed his initials, sometimes also with the date, and once with "de Scherding". 19th-century English red morocco, back elaborately gilt, supralibros in gilt of Earl Spencer on the sides, g.e., marbled endpapers, by Samuel Charles Kalthoeber, with his gold stamp on verso of first free endleaf. From the libraries of Louis de la Baume le Blanc, Duc de la Vallière (his sale, Paris, Dec. 1783, lot 4591); and of George John, Earl Spencer, with his small leather bookplate; release label of the John Rylands University Library, Manchester.

Fine, large copy of the first edition, the third book from the press of Johann Schüssler, who had begun printing in Augsburg the previous year.

The rubricator, Georgius Sparsguet, announces himself on one leaf as being from Schärding, an old town on the river Inn very close to the Austro-German border. He has dated his rubrication in three places with "1473", two years after the book was printed. The work is dedicated to St. Augustine, who suggested it as a theme to Paulus Orosius (fl. 415), the Spanish historian and theologian, when the latter consulted him at Hippo. He stayed some time in Africa as a disciple of Augustine, then went on to Palestine with a letter of introduction to Jerome. Here he became involved in the Pelagian controversy on the side of Augustine.

His book is an attempt to prove that the condition of the world had not been worsened by the introduction of Christianity, as the pagans said, but that on the contrary mankind had always been beset by calamities and that now there was the countervailing promise of life after death.

A handsomely rubricated, wide-margined copy with a fine provenance.

H 12101; BMC II, 328; Goff O-96; BNIC O-58; Pol 4619; IGI 7033; IDL 3450; Bénédictins du Bouveret II, 5149.

26 CASSIODORUS, MAGNUS AURELIUS. In hoc corpore contin­entur tripertite historie ex Socrate Sozomeno et Theodorico in unu[m] collecte et nuper de greco in latinu[m] translate libri numero duodecim.

Augsburg, Johann Schüssler, 'Circiter' 5 February 1472

Folio (317 × 210 mm.). Gothic type. 35 lines. [192] ff. (of 195, lacking first and last two blanks). 2 large 7-line painted initials, one in green and red and other in blue and red. Occasional early marginalia in a small, neat hand. Light tan morocco back and corners with beige cloth sides. From the Pier­pont Morgan library, with its release note.

First edition, translated from the Greek, of the ecclesiastical histories of Theo­doretus, Sozomenus and Socrates, covering the period 306-439, compiled under the supervision of Cassiodorus.

This is a very fine copy, with large margins. Schüssler's gothic type was apparently taken over from Günther Zainer, who last used it in January 1470.

HC 4573; GW 6164; BMC II, 329; Goff C-237; Pel 3349; IGI 2553; IDL 1163.

A FINE WOODCUT INCUNABULUM IN A CONTEMPORARY BINDING

27 ANGELUS, JOHANNES. Astrolabium planu[m].

Augsburg, Erhard Ratdolt, [6 October?] 1488

4to (217 × 160 mm.). Gothic type. 40 lines. [175] ff. (of 176, lacking final blank; small blank portion missing from title fore edge; occasional damp­marks in fore margins). 439 woodcuts, numerous floriated woodcut initials white on black, a few cuts and initials nicely colored by hand. Contempo­rary roll-stamped South German binding of morocco over wooden boards (top and bottom of spine defective); outer border of flowers and leafy scrolls with tiny birds, central panel of four (upper cover) and three (lower cover) vertical rolls of urns and flowers, roll-stamp of scroll stems and flowers be­tween panel and border (upper) and single rose stamps on lower cover. One brass-and-leather clasp (of four), two brass catches (of four). Some early ms. notes concerning the periods covered by the signs of the zodiac on rear flyleaf. From the Samuel Hoffman Collection at N.Y. Hist. Soc. (sale, Christie, London, 12 Nov. 1975, lot 2).

First edition of this significant astronomical work. The *Astrolabium* of Johan­nes Angelus (Engel, 1463-1512) is a famous woodcut book displaying a remark­able collection of mediaeval and renaissance imagery. The cuts show mostly men, women, and animals, but occasionally objects or buildings, enclosed within horoscopes and with descriptions.

The attractive contemporary, probably original, binding of dark brown calf is most likely from Augsburg and two of the tools correspond to Kyriss pl. 175. These are the roll-stamp scroll of flowers with scrolls and tiny birds, and the single six-petalled rose stamp.

GW 1900; H 1100; BMC II, 382; Goff A-711; Pell 759; Pol 203; IGI 374; Stillwell (Science) 51; Klebs 375.1; Houzeau-Lancaster 3252; Zinner 320; Essling 432; Schramm XXIII, 25; Schreiber 3316; Fairfax Murray I, 39; Kyriss 86, pl. 173, nos. 1 and 6.

IN THE ORIGINAL SOUTH GERMAN BINDING

28 ANGELUS DE CLAVASIO. Summa angelica de casibus conscientiae.

Nuremberg, Anton Koberger, 28 August 1488

Folio (310 × 210 mm.). Gothic type. 61 lines. 2 cols. 310 ff., plus first and last blanks (occasional light browning or spotting). Opening initial "A" in burnished gold on a white-ornamented rose ground, with border of blue, green, and yellow, leafy scrolls of pink, lilac, and green extending down the inner margin; initials supplied in red, some with penwork flourishes, also 2 in blue. Original German blind-stamped pigskin over wooden boards; large central panels of intertwining cusped stems, each with plant resembling an artichoke in the central oval formed by the intersecting stems; outer border of a stag leaping a wattle fence (all stamps in Kyriss II, 80); remnants of brass clasps (rubbed and with some wear at edges, but quite sound); title in contemporary ms. on front cover. Ms. exlibris of Monastery of the Reformed Franciscans (17th century) of Bolzano (formerly southern Tyrol), with their bookplate on inside front cover.

Angelus Carletus (d. 1495), later known as Clavasio (after his birthplace, Chivasso, near Genoa) was a Franciscan and is chiefly known through the present work. He compiled it with the aim of replacing the numerous and sometimes rambling Summae and Confessionales by a single authoritative book. A very useful inclusion is the section of *Interrogationes*, which is a complete listing of all general and special questions of the confessor, with references to those parts of the text where more detailed information may be obtained. The *Rubricae iuris civilis et canonici* are added at the end. Such was the reputation and importance of this work that it was singled out by Luther in his attack on the Church's position on penitence and good works; it should rather be called *Summa plusquam diabolica* he said, and burned a copy in Wittenberg in 1520.

GW 1927; HC 5385; BMC II, 432; Goff A-717; IGI 563; Hase 124.

29 PETRUS LOMBARDUS. – ST. BONAVENTURA, *comm*; BECKENHAUB, JOHANNES, *ed.* Sententiarum libri IV.

[Nuremberg, Anton Koberger, after 2 March 1491]

Folio (314 × 215 mm.). Gothic type. Text of each distinctio of Petrus is printed with side-notes on the inner margin and gloss on the outer margin and below, and is followed by the quaestiones of Bonaventura in 2 columns. 55 lines text, 63 commentary. 2 (of 5) vols. in 1: [204; 260] ff. (some worming in first two leaves affecting a few letters of text, continuing for a few leaves more in margins; first 2 quires lightly waterstained in outermost lower fore-edge margin). Initials supplied in red, capitals touched in red; contemporary marginalia. Original blind-stamped pigskin monastic binding, with four brass corner bosses on front cover and central bosses on both covers (corner bosses lacking on back cover); leather-and-brass clasps and brass catches; both covers with different single stamps in panels, employing a unicorn, a double-eagle, a stemmed flower with a raised center, and a small dragon, all in lozenges; in a rectangle a blossom with a broad leaf above; a small four-petalled flower and another six-petalled; a rose, and a six-pointed star. From the monastic library of St. Mang at Füssen.

The first edition of the *Sententiae* with the commentary of Bonaventura. Written in the middle of the twelfth century, this collection of opinions of the Fathers of the Church became one of the most famous text-books of the Middle Ages, and many noted theologians wrote a commentary on them. So famous were they that Peter Lombard was known as *Magister sententiarum.*

The present monastic binding is a particularly fine example, rich in a variety of single stamps of great delicacy and intricacy. Two of the stamps are found on Kyriss pl. 51, a Carmelite monastery in Nuremberg, one on pl. 53, a Carthusian monastery in the same city, and one on pl. 319, unidentified workshop.

HC 3540; BMC II, 433; Goff P-486; Pell 2714; Pol 795; IGI 7643; IDL 3666; Hase 132.

THE ONLY VELLUM COPY IN THE U.S. OF STUCHS'S FIRST BOOK

30 MISSALE ROMANUM. (*Inc.:*) Incipit ordo missalis s[ecundu]m consuetudinem romane curie.

Nuremberg, Georg Stuchs, 1484

4to (205 × 150 mm.). Gothic type. 30 lines. 2 cols. [256] ff., incl. blank ff. [1] and [8] (two natural vellum flaws affecting a few letters). Seven-line initial "A" on opening text page with acanthus leaf scroll in lower and right margins, in burnished gold, pink, green, violet and yellow, by a south

German artist; 15 initials (3- to 6-line) supplied in blue with red infill; 2-line lombardic capitals and rubrics printed in red; calendar in black and red. 19th-cent. dark brown morocco by Bedford, panelled and gold-stamped with fleurons in the outer angles and leafy sprays with angel heads in the inner (joints a little rubbed), g.e. In morocco-backed drop-box. Contemporary or early ms. inscription in German on first leaf. From the libraries of Sir John Horner (his sale, Sotheby, 20 April 1921, lot 501); and of Estelle Doheny, with her leather bookplate.

The first book printed by Georg Stuchs who was one of the most important liturgical printers in Germany until the second decade of the sixteenth century.

Copies on vellum are very rare (Van Praet lists only four altogether) and this is the only one recorded in Goff. Oddly enough, it does not appear in the Doheny Catalogue.

A very handsome example of liturgical printing, with fine lombardic initials in red throughout.

HC 11384; BMC II, 467; Goff M-697; BNIC M-456; IGI 6612; IDL 3246; Weale-Bohatta 890; Van Praet (Roi) I, no. 89.

Exaudi nos   Oratio.
Domine sancte pater oi-
potens eterne deus. et mittere
digneris sanctum angelu tuu
de celis. qui custodiat foueat
protegat visitet ⁊ defendat om
nes habitantes in hoc habita
culo. Per christum dominu
nostrum. Amen.

30 Missale Romanum on vellum

31 GUILLERMUS ALVERNUS, BISHOP OF PARIS. De sacramentis. Cur deus homo et de penitencia cum registro.

[Nuremberg, Georg Stuchs, not after 1497]

Folio (297 × 200 mm.). Gothic type. 54 lines. 2 cols. [3], 132 ff. (lacking the fourth leaf, a blank; a few insignificant worm-holes occasionally touch-ing a letter of text).

(Bound with:) GUILLERMUS ALVERNUS, BISHOP OF PARIS. De universo. Pars prima.

[Nuremberg, Georg Stuchs, not after 1497]

[2], 149, [1] ff., including f. 2 blank. This and the preceding work with opening initials to each part in blue with pale red penwork decoration;

smaller initials in red, some paragraph marks in red, all in the same hand. 18th-century brown calf (rubbed and scuffed). Exlibris on title of Fratres Colareensis (?).

First edition of two works by the learned scholastic William of Auvergne, (born c. 1180), bishop of Paris from 1228 until his death in 1249. At the end is added the last part of *Opera de Fide*, [Nuremberg, G. Stuchs, after 31 March, 1496], entitled *De immortalitate animae*, consisting of 30 ff. including the Register by Johann Rosenbach. William of Auvergne was deeply read in occult lore; he was well acquainted, for example, with the works of Hermes Trismegistus. His *De universo* deals rather more with the world of nature than do his other treatises which are more theological in content.

The exlibris is hard to interpret. It might possibly be Colania or Coldingham in Scotland where there was a Benedictine abbey. A nice example of the printing of Georg Stuchs, with wide margins surrounding the regular masses of type.

Ad I: HC 8316; BMC II, 470; Goff G-723; IDL 2172; W. Baumann, "Die Druckerei Stuchs zu Nürnberg (1484–1537) in *Gutenberg-Jb.* (1954), pp. 122–132, no. 72.

Ad II: HC 8319; BMC II, 470; Goff G-717; IDL 2174; W. Baumann, op cit., no. 74.

32 VOCABULARY. – Vocabularius juris utriusque.

[Speyer, Peter Drach, c. 1477]

Small folio (282 × 200 mm.). Gothic type. 40 lines. [247] ff. including first blank (few insignificant wormholes in first and last few leaves; small tear repaired in inner margin of first 3 leaves and small stain on same leaves). Large opening initial Q supplied in red, with red penwork infilling and extenders; other large initials in red and white; paragraph marks in red and capitals touched in red. Contemporary blind-stamped dark brown calf over bevelled wooden boards (rebacked, original backstrip laid down; clasps lacking; some worm punctures, rubbed); paste-downs from an early vellum text ms. Early ms. exlibris inked over on front endleaf and on first text leaf; library label of the Dukes of Arenberg on spine.

A fine copy of this valuable vocabulary. In spite of its title it is by no means restricted to legal terminology, defining also words like pedagogus, vinum, metallum, etc.

The upper cover of the binding has a central panel with lozenges formed by quadruple rules, in the middle of each of which is a single stamp of a rose in a circle; this central panel is surrounded by a roll-stamp border of leafy scrolls and stems; the lower cover is composed of lozenges also formed by quadruple rules, with various single stamps in the center of each – a lion, a pelican, and some animal seated upright, perhaps a monkey. Although the binding shows some wear this is generally a fine fresh copy of a scarce book.

There is no copy in BMC and only 3 copies in Goff, one of which is incomplete.

R 1105; Goff V-337; Pol 4022; IDL 4694.

A BROADSIDE FROM SPEYER

33 SIXTUS IV (POPE) Copia l[itte]rarum sub forma brevis Sanctissimi d[omi]ni nostri Pape a[n]nulo piscatoris sigillataru[m] suspe[n]sionis omniu[m] aliaru[m] indulgentiaru[m] durantibus indulge[n]tiis in favore[m] civitatis et insule Rhodi concessaru[m] [et]c.

[Speyer, Peter Drach, after 1 July 1480]

Broadside. 297 × 209 mm. (some worm-punctures affecting 3 letters and a few marginal worm-tracks). Gothic type in three sizes. 30 lines. With the control signature of the notary Johann Sybolt. Matted, in a red half-morocco slipcase. From the collections of the Württembergische Landesbibliothek, Stuttgart, with their stamp and release mark; of Otto Vollbehr; and of Estelle Doheny, with her leather booklabel.

A rare incunabular broadside, unknown to the *Gesamtkatalog* or any incunabula bibliography other than Goff who lists the present copy only. It is an indulgence letter, issued by Pope Sixtus IV (regnal years 1471-1484) on behalf of the city and island of Rhodes, then besieged by Turkish forces, suspending all indulgences except those in favor of the defense of Rhodes. In the letter, the pope gives permission for the text to be published in the various countries of Christendom, as long as each copy is signed by the local bishop or other official. The present copy is signed by the public notary Johann Sybolt. The "L. Grifus" whose name appears at the end of the letter was Leonardo Grifo, the pope's private secretary.

Six copies of the present broadside were discovered bound into the covers of an incunable in the Württembergische Landesbibliothek, which originally came from the Cistercian monastery of Schöntal an der Jagst (35 miles southwest of Würzburg), and indeed, one copy bore the crest of that institution. Three of them were released by the library through exchange.

Goff S-561 (this copy); O. Leuze, "Zehn Jahre Makulaturforschung in der Inkunabelsammlung der Württ. Landesbibliothek in Stuttgart," in *Zentralblatt für Bibliothekswesen* 48 (1931), p. 7, no. 4; not in GW or *Einblattdrucke*.

34   THOMAS AQUINAS. Catena aurea [super quattuor evangelistas].

[Esslingen, Conrad Fyner, c. 1475]

Large thick folio (408 × 285 mm.). Gothic type. 60 lines of commentary type. 2 cols. [417] ff., some leaves uncut (first and last leaves a little soiled, and small hole repaired in first leaf with a few letters in pen facsimile; occasional spotting in first quire, last few leaves faintly waterstained in lower blank margin). 6 large woodcut initials, 4 of them with animal or plant decoration, 2 of them colored in pink and blue, and numerous smaller woodcut initials, all in unusual style; some leaves rubricated (see below). Sixteenth-century blind-stamped pigskin; upper cover with six roll-stamps forming panels; lower cover with 3 roll-stamps and diagonal triple rules forming lozenges in the center (some cracks and rubbing, clasps lacking).

The term *Catena* denotes a collection of Bible commentaries arranged in chain-like succession, a practice that began early in the West in the sixth century. St. Thomas, however, may be said to have brought it to its highest form by including eighty Greek and Latin authors in this work, and quoting them verbatim. Such a compilation represents a truly monumental piece of scholarship, encompassing all four Gospels, each with its own index. The work is especially important because many of the texts quoted are no longer extant.

This is a very stately book from the press of Esslingen's first printer, on beautiful crisp paper, partially uncut. The unusual initials include an outline E showing a tree, a D and I with acorns, an L with a dog, an R and foliated S. It is thought that Fyner served his apprenticeship at Strassburg in the printing office of Heinrich Eggestein and his first type is undoubtedly modelled on Eggestein's Type 3.

It is interesting to note that the few rubricated leaves are invariably the first four leaves in the 10-leaf quires [a]-[g]; this pattern may offer some important clues as to the work routine in a rubricator's shop.

HC1329; BMC II, 515; Goff T-228; Pell 933; IDL 4351; on Fyner see Victor Scholderer, "Notes on the Incunabula of Esslingen" *Gutenberg-Jb.*, 1950, pp. 167–171.

34   Thomas Aquinas

35   CONRADUS DE BRUNDELSHEIM (SOCCUS). Sermones no⁓
tabiles et formales Fr[atr]is Socci ordinis cystersiencium de Sanctis.

[Reutlingen, Michael Greyff, not after 1478]

Folio (296 × 220 mm.). Gothic type. 42 lines. [242] ff. (first leaf a little soiled;
occasional small stains and thumbing marks). Initials (some with penwork
extensions) and paragraph marks supplied in red; capitals touched in red;
original quiring in red by rubricator and signatures also numbered in black
(these marks occasionally shaved at lower edge). Original blind⁓stamped
pigskin, either German or Netherlandish; covers divided into lozenges
which are filled with single stamps of a bird (phoenix), a crayfish, a rose and
fleur⁓de⁓lys, the crayfish and fleur⁓de⁓lys in diamond shapes, the other two
in circular stamps (scuffed and rubbed, worn at edges, but sound; small
piece lacking from upper center back where chain was fastened); two brass
catches and one clasp. Some contemporary marginalia. From the libraries of
the Benedictine Abbey of St. Matthias at Trier, with its elegantly written
contemporary ms. exlibris on recto of first leaf; of the monastery at Gmünden,
with its ms. exlibris at top of first text leaf; and of Georg Kloss (his sale, 1835,
lot 3555), with shelfmark and Panzer number in his hand.

One of the first two books printed at Reutlingen; the date comes from a copy
at Leipzig which has "1478" in manuscript. The second edition of the *Sermons
of the Saints* by Conrad of Brundelsheim, abbot of the Cistercians at Heilbronn
(South Germany); he died in 1321.

Of particular interest in the binding is the small crayfish stamp which we
have not found recorded.

GW 7412; H 14829⁓30; BMC II, 574; Goff S⁓585; Pell 3929; IGI 1373.

36 JOHANNES FRIBURGENSIS. – BERTHOLD, *tr.* Summa [con‑
fessorum]. (Inc.) Hir heuet sitz an de vorrede disses bokes genomet Summa
Johannis . . . Un[d] va[n] latine in dat dudesche gemaket dorch eine[m]
hoch gelerden doctore[m].

Magdeburg, Moritz Brandis, 21 Sept. 1491

Folio (250 × 193 mm.). Gothic type. 42 lines. 2 cols. [158] ff. (title some‑
what soiled; very occasional light spotting; small repair to blank fore‑edge
of title; few tiny worm‑punctures in first few leaves). Large foliated woodcut
initials, black with white outline and foliation on black ground; smaller
unframed ones, and plain black calligraphic ones. Modern boards with pig‑
skin back. Faded contemporary exlibris and an early note to the effect that
on the octave of St. Augustine, Heinrich Vesteller (?) gave 6 talents.

This is the first dated book printed by Moritz Brandis after his migration from
Leipzig to Magdeburg and apparently the first to use woodcut initials. The types
are a large‑face missal, used for headings, and a smaller gothic text type, not
illustrated in BMC, but similar to Koch 97. The large woodcut initials are
particularly handsome.

The German translation of Johannes Friburgensis (d. 1314) first appeared in
print in 1472, four years before the Latin version. Written in the very early four‑
teenth century and translated about a hundred years later by the Dominican monk
Berthold, the work is a manual for confessors, with the material arranged in
alphabetical order. The material covers a wide range of everyday problems and
includes medical and legal advice.

H 7375; Goff J‑323 (listing only 1 defective copy); Borchling & Clausen 188; Scheller
444; Not in BMC, BN, IGI or IDL.

37 ALBERTANUS CAUSIDICUS BRIXIENSIS. Tractatus de arte
loquendi et tacendi.

Memmingen, Albrecht Kunne, 1489

8 vo (189 × 129 mm.). Gothic type. 42 lines. 2 cols. [15] pp. Some annota‑
tions in two later hands on last leaf. Limp vellum, silk ties.

A mediaeval moral treatise on the art of when to speak and when to keep
silent, by Albertano da Brescia (fl.1215‑1253). When studying law in the judge's
college of Brescia he was inscribed in the Corporation of "causidici", which
trained men for roles in public life in the Commune. He held various official
posts for Brescia and Genoa. According to the colophon, he wrote the present
work for the instruction of his children.

GW 547; H 404; BMC II, 605; Goff A‑200 (only 2 copies); Pell 261; IGI 146.

38 PIUS II [AENEAS SILVIUS PICCOLOMINI]. Opuscula Enee Silvii de duobus amantibus Et de remedio amoris cu[m] ep[isto]la retracta‑ toria eiusdem Pii secu[n]di ad quenda[m] karolum.

Leipzig, Conrad Kachelofen, [c. 1489‑1495]

Small 4to (208 × 145 mm.). Gothic type. 40 lines. [46] pp., 1 blank f. (title lightly soiled, marginal worm‑puncture). 19th‑century green half vellum, gold‑lettered title on spine. From the libraries of A. H. Bates, with his ms. exlibris; and of Joseph Nève (Brussels), with his bookplate.

An early edition of the celebrated love story written by a future pope; it is one of the first novels in the modern sense and is based upon a true story, an amorous adventure of the German Chancellor Gaspar Schlick, a friend of Piccolomini's, with a Siennese lady. First published c. 1473, it was often reprinted and translated in the fifteenth century.

This edition also includes his *De remedio amoris* and a letter to Karolus Cypria‑ cus retracting that treatise.

On the first and last page of this copy are 4 lines each of blind impression of standing type.

This is the only copy recorded in Polain, and Polain‑Suppl. lists it as "perdue".

H 226; BMC III, 632; Goff P‑682 (LC only); Pell 160 (1 copy); Pol 3157; IGI 7808.

39 BALTHASAR DE PORTA. Expositio cano[n]is sacratissime misse.

[Leipzig], Conrad Kachelofen, 1497

4to (197 × 135 mm.). Gothic types. 18 and 42 lines for text and commen‑ tary respectively. [20] ff. One criblé initial pasted in, partly colored in red. Blind‑tooled antique calf, gold‑stamped title on upper cover.

A popular running commentary on the Canon of the Roman Mass by Bal‑ thasar de Porta, a Cistercian theologian and educator of Leipzig. Short sections of the text of the Canon are printed in large display type, followed by Balthasar's commentary on each section printed in smaller type.

The work's popularity is evident from the quick succession of editions, all in Leipzig, where it must have been intended for classroom use. The first edition appeared in 1495.

GW 3218; H 2346; Goff B‑40; not in BMC.

40 BALTHASAR DE PORTA. Expositio misterioru[m] misse.cristi passione[m] devotissime figurantiu[m].metrice at q[ue] prosaice posita.

Leipzig, Gregorius Böttiger (Werman), [14]95

Small 4to (216 × 151 mm.). Gothic type. 34 lines. [28] ff. (few insignificant stains on first leaf). Large woodcut initial 'E' at beginning of text. Tan morocco. Neat marginalia in red and black in two early hands, with occaʼ sional underlining in red. Bookplate and small library stamp of Albert Ehrman, and Broxbourne library bookplate of John Ehrman.

A commentary on the Canon of the Mass by Balthasar de Porta (fl. 1487–1499), Provisor of the Cistercian College of St. Bernard in Leipzig. Sections of varying length of the text of the Canon, printed in large size type, are followed by commentary in a smaller size. There were numerous editions, all printed in Leipzig, which suggests that the text was used by students at the University.

Laid in is a typed letter from the Kommission für den Gesamtkatalog der Wiegendrucke, signed by Max Joseph Husung, dated 12 Feb. 1927, to Albert Ehrman concerning this book.

HC 2348; GW 3223; Goff Bʼ43; Pell 1754; not in BMC.

41 TRITHEMIUS, JOHANNES. De laudibus sanctissime matris Anne tractat[us].

Leipzig, Melchior Lotter, [after 21 July 1494]

Small 4to (213 × 152 mm.). Gothic types. 42ʼ43 lines. [24] ff. (piece torn from fore margin of C₄, barely touching 2 letters of text; stain on A₃ʼ₅; paper a little darkened). Initials and paragraph marks supplied in red or blue, headings underlined in red. Calf.

First Lotter edition of this hagiographical work by the Abbot of Sponheim. In his Epistola at the beginning of the work, Trithemius states that it was written at the behest of Rumold Laupach, Prior of the Carmelite order at Frankfurt. He also says that miracles by St. Anne have been rejected so that the educated who do not find it easy to believe in them will not mistrust his treatise. At the end of the Epistola is the date kalendis Julias, Anno d[omi]ni M.cccc.xciiii. The last part of the work is devoted to poems in praise of St. Anne by the author himself, by Conrad Celtis and by Rudolph Agricola, among others.

The edition of this work printed by Petrus Friedberg in Mainz is dated XII kal. Augusti (21 July) 1494, and it seems quite likely that the work appeared almost simultaneously in both Mainz and Leipzig. However, the Mainz edition does not have the epilogue to the Reader which is present in our edition, so this is certainly the earliest edition with the full text.

In the *Gutenberg Jahrbuch* of 1972, F. Juntke has an article on the Lotter editions of this work in which he lists two variants. Our copy does not agree wholly with either of his, but the article contains several misprints and inconsistencies so that it is impossible to know exactly what the author means.

H 15631; BMC III, 652 (Epistola with year not given); Goff T-446 (which version is not clear); Pol 3813 (same version as BMC); F. Juntke, "Über die Schrift . . . De Laudibus S. Annae" *GJ*, (1972), pp. 98–101.

ONE OF ONLY THREE BOOKS PRINTED AT STUTTGART IN THE
FIFTEENTH CENTURY

42 CYPRIANUS, CAECILIUS. Opera.

[Stuttgart, Printer of the "Erwählung Maximilians", c. 1486]

Folio (296 × 207 mm.). Gothic type. 45-47 lines. 2 cols. [132] ff., including first blank, uncut (A$_1$ and R$_5$ strengthened at inner margin; R$_2$ repaired in lower and R$_6$ in upper corner; small light brown stain in upper inner margin of several leaves; some leaves browned due to faulty paper, occurring in most copies). Contemporary foliation (incorrect) in red; contemporary marginalia in a small neat hand, also numbering of Table of Contents. Late sixteenth-century blind-stamped pigskin over bevelled wooden boards (some rubbing); two leather-and-brass clasps and catches.

One of only three books attributed on the basis of type to the sole incunabular press in Stuttgart, now thought to be possibly that of Johann Scheffer or Scheffler. The type is the same as that in a pamphlet describing the election of Maximilian as King of the Romans in 1486, with a colophon stating that it was printed in Stuttgart, but not mentioning the name of the printer.

The colophon in this copy has the misprint "Ccilij . . . cōfossoris" for "Cecilij . . . cōfessoris", probably making it the first issue of this edition, which is one of only five printed in the fifteenth century, although St. Cyprian, Bishop of Carthage (d. 258), was one of the foremost figures of the early Church.

A crisp, uncut and desirable copy in a well-preserved binding.

GW 7887; HC 5895 (with our colophon); BMC III, 675; Goff C-1014; Pell 4075 (with our colophon); Pol 1209; IDL 1452; Geldner I, p. 271, illus. 108 (for the type).

43   HOLCOT, ROBERT. Super sapientiam Salomonis.

Hagenau, [Heinrich Gran], 1494

Folio (285 × 200 mm.). Gothic type. 54 lines. 2 cols. [242] ff. (occasional light soiling and thumbing, one leaf stained at bottom). Lombardic initials supplied in red; few paragraph marks in red. Contemporary and early marginalia in both red and black ink.
(*Bound with*:) ALBERTUS MAGNUS. Opus insigne de laudibus beate marie virginis; alias Mariale appellatu[m].

Strassburg, Martin Flach, 1493

Gothic type. 52-53 lines. [300] ff., including final blank (few leaves lightly browned). Large initials in red and blue, smaller initials in red or blue; paragraph marks in red. Sixteenth-century blind-stamped pigskin with various rolls of flowers and scrolls. On lower edge an early ms. exlibris of Fr. Jo. (Frater Johann); on inside back cover another ownership mark of a cross in a circle over XO (Christo).

The first item has a rather misleading title and is actually a commentary on the Bible, arranged for the use of students and preachers in a series of *lectiones*. Holcot's work reveals an extraordinary variety of sources – Aristotle, Seneca, Bede, Ovid, Macrobius, Virgil, Valerius Maximus, Cicero, Hermes Trismegistus, Averroes and Solinus to name but a few. A Dominican doctor of theology at Oxford, Holcot (d. 1349) was one of Ockham's pupils and is believed by some to be the real author of the *Philobiblon*, which is generally ascribed to Richard de Bury, Bishop of Durham. R. L. Poole, in his article on Holcot for the DNB refers to a title for the *Philobiblon* found in several manuscripts which states "Incipit prologus Philobiblon Ricardi Dunelmensis episcopi, quem librum compilavit Robertus Holcote de ordine predicatorum sub nomine dicti episcopi". In other words, Holcot wrote the book at the request of and in the name of the bishop.

The second work by Albertus Magnus is in praise of the Virgin Mary, in which is included quite a lot of natural history of plants, trees, herbs, etc.

Ad I: HC 8761; BMC III, 683; Goff H-293; IGI 4793; IDL 2744
Ad II: HC (Add.) 10767 = 10768; BMC I, 152; GW 616/10; Goff A-248; Schmidt 45.

44   SUMMENHART, KONRAD. Septipartitu[m] opus de contractibus pro foro co[n]scientie et theologico.

Hagenau, Heinrich Gran, 13 October 1500

Folio (286 × 200 mm.). Gothic type. 51 lines. 2 cols. [433] ff. (of 434, lacking final blank; few worm-punctures at beginning and end, occasionally affecting a letter of text; few leaves with light waterstaining in bottom margin). One large 9-line opening text initial in blue and white with red penwork; several smaller red or blue initials at beginning of text divisions. Modern calf in the style of the period, with brass clasps.

First edition of a very interesting work on the law and ethics of commercial contracts. It is divided into seven parts dealing with thirty different kinds of contracts recognised by the author - loans and usury, buying and selling by merchants, the purchase of annuities, contracts of hiring and leasing, partnerships and similar associations, and money and exchange.

The BMC calls for two leaves less, having only 6 instead of 8 leaves in quire e, and they do not indicate anything lacking. However, the collation in NUC is identical with ours, so it would seem the BMC entry is in error. It does not appear likely that this quire of 8 leaves could be reset in 6 for some copies.

Konrad Summenhart (d. 1502) was a professor at the newly founded Tübingen University in 1478. A few years later he became Rector and in 1489 received his doctorate in Theology. From the standpoint of his time, his work is greatly esteemed, most particularly his theories on usury.

HC 15179; BMC III, 688; Goff S-863; Pol 3637; IGI 9217; IDL 4254; Kress S. 3.

THE FIRST BOOK PRINTED IN FREIBURG

45 GUILLERMUS ALVERNUS (BISHOP OF PARIS). Rethorica Divina de Oratione domini Guilermi Parisien[sis].

[Freiburg im Breisgau, Kilian Fischer, not after 1491]

Small folio (283 × 197 mm.). Gothic type. 52 lines. 2 cols. [58] ff. (washed, causing occasional light smudging of rubrication, one worm-puncture in lower margin, some light marginal soiling). Many 3- and 4-line initials in red or blue, the first extending out into the margin, chapter headings underlined and capitals touched in red; a vividly rendered bird, apparently by the rubricator, in lower margin of f.2; biographical note in an old German hand in lower margin of title. Polished blind-ruled calf antique.

Considered the first book printed in Freiburg im Breisgau, this is one of four or five undated books printed by Kilian Fischer.

Guillaume d'Auvergne (d. 1249) bishop of Paris, was the author of several influential exegetical and instructional works for the clergy. He is one of the most important figures during the period of transition between the early scholasticism of the twelfth century, and the high scholasticism of Bonaventura and Aquinas. He is unfortunately sometimes confused with a Guillermus Parisiensis, author (in 1437) of the best-selling *Postilla*.

HC 8303; BMC III, 693; Goff G-714; Pol 1808; IGI 4605.

46   BIEL, GABRIEL. Epithoma expositionis Canonis misse.

Tübingen, [Johann Ottmar for Friedrich Meynberger, c. 1500]

Small 4to (200 × 145 mm.). Gothic type. 37 lines. [78] ff., including final blank, uncut (few worm-punctures in fore margin; light waterstain in upper portion of last few leaves). Large Crucifixion woodcut on A₅ᵛ, and 2 woodcut initials including a "T" with a snake draped over it. Vellum. With some contemporary marginalia.

The second, revised edition by Ottmar, and the first to employ the large Crucifixion woodcut. It is set up leaf for leaf from Ottmar's other edition (after 20 February and before 29 November 1499), except that the Prologus is printed on f. 6r and it has the woodcut on 5ᵛ; the errata at the end are omitted, having been presumably corrected. As BMC notes, the two editions are evidently not far apart in time. We are able to date the earlier edition from Wendelin Stainbach's letter to Friedrich Meynberger, the bookseller, dated from Tübingen, 20 February 1499, and from Stainbach's letter to the publisher in Biel's *Expositio missae*, dated 29 November 1499, mentioning an edition of the *Epitoma* as already published.

Ottmar's was the only incunabular press in Tübingen. He came there from Reutlingen and completed his first book in March 1498. He continued to print for the University until 1501.

Gabriel Biel (c. 1425-1495), known as "the last of the scholastics", was instrumental in founding the University of Tübingen, where he became its first professor of theology. Included in the present volume are verses by his friend Heinrich Bebel, and the letter from Wendelin Stainbach, the editor (referred to above), to the bookseller Friedrich Meynberger.

GK 4336; H 3180; BMC III, 702; Goff B-656; Pell 2391; IGI 1715; IDL 876; Schramm IX, p. 17, illus. 846; Schreiber 3490; Steiff 16.

⚜ ITALY ⚜

MAGNIFICENT WIDE-MARGINED COPY

47   AUGUSTINUS, AURELIUS. De civitate dei.

Rome, Conrad Sweynheym & Arnold Pannartz, 1470

Folio (403 × 277 mm.). Roman type. 46 lines. [290] ff. (of 294, lacking
the 4 blanks at ff. 1, 16, 293 and 294; few negligible damp-marks in some
lower outer corners; small area of restoration in lower blank margin of first
leaf). Large illuminated 15-line initial "I" on f. 17, in purple, green, and
burnished gold, with the decoration continuing below to form an inner
border; on same leaf a 9-line initial "G" in blue and white on a red penwork
ground; several 7-line red-and-white or blue-and-white initials, and numerous 2-line solid initials in red or blue; chapter headings flourished in red or
blue. Binding by Douglas Cockerell of half tan morocco, tooled in blind
and gold, over oak boards, plaited leather clasps and metal catches, signed
on inside lower cover with his monogram and date of 1903; marginal sum-
maries in an elegant contemporary hand in the first part of the book. From
the library of Martin Bodmer, with his shelf-mark and ms. notes.

A splendid copy of St. Augustine's great treatise in vindication of Christianity
and the Church, it being taller and wider than either of the two in BMC. The
penwork initials are very finely executed and add color to the beautifully propor-
tioned type-page.

The binding is a superb example of Cockerell's work that manages to be of
its time and yet amply suggest the fifteenth century. The half morocco is tooled in
blind in an interlace pattern, with tiny gold leaves and circles, and a narrow
vertical band of dots and oval leaves, this latter identical to an illustration of a
Cockerell binding in his *Bookbinding and the Care of Books*, pl. V. The half leather
inside is decorated with a column of Tudor roses and leaves. In 1903 Cockerell
was working in his own studio in London, having left the Doves Bindery in
1898.

A magnificent copy of a great work produced by the first Roman printers.

GW 2876; HC 2049; BMC IV, 10–11; Goff A-1232; Pell 1548; Pol 356; IGI 968;
IDL 489.

Voniã cóſtat omiũ rerũ optandarũ plenitudinẽ eſſe felicitatẽ:
que nó eſt dea:ſed donũ dei:& ideo nullũ deum colendũ eſſe ab
hominibuſ:niſi q̃ pót eoſ facere felices. Vnde ſi illa dea eſſet:ſola
colenda merito diceretur. Iam cóſequenter uideamuſ:qua cauſa
deuſ qui pót & illa bona dare: que habere poſſunt etiã nó boni
ac per hoc etiã nó felices: Romanũ imperiũ tã magnum tamq;
diuturnũ eſſe uoluerit. Quia enim hoc deorũ falſorũ illa quam
colebãt: multitudo nó fecit:& multa tã diximuſ:& ubi uiſum fuerit opportunũ eſſe:
dicemuſ. Cauſa ergo magnitudiniſ Impii Romani nec fortuita eſt: nec fataliſ ſcdm
eorũ ſentẽtiã:ſiue opinionẽ q̃ ea dicũt ẽ fortuita: que uel nullaſ cauſaſ habẽt uel nó
ex aliquo rationabili ordine ueniẽteſ:& ea fatalia:que pter dei & hominũ uolũtatẽ
cuiuſdã ordiniſ neceſſitate cótingũt. Prorſuſ diuina prouidentia regna cóſtituuntur
humana. Que ſi ppterea quiſq̃ fato tribuit: qa ipſam dei uolũtatem uel ptãrem fati
nomie appellat:ſentẽtiã teneat·linguã corrigat. Cur·n·nó hoc p̃mũ dicat qd̃ poſtea
dicturuſ eſt:cũ ab illo quiſq̃ q̃ſierit qd dixerit fatũ? Nam id homineſ qñ audiunt
uſitata loquẽdi cóſuetudine· nó intelligũt niſi uim poſitióiſ ſiderũ q̃liſ ẽ qñ q̃ſ naſcit̃:
ſiue cócipit̃. qd̃ aliqui alienãt a dei uolũtate:aliq̃ ex illa etiã hec pendere cófirmant.
Sed illi qui ſine dei uolũtate decernere opinant̃ ſidera qd̃ agamuſ: uel qd̃ bonorum
habeamuſ:malorũ ue patiamur:ab auribuſ omniũ repellẽdi ſũt. Nó ſolũ eorũ q̃ uerã
religiõe tenẽt: ſed q̃ deorũ q̃liũ cunq̃ licet falſorũ uolũt eſſe cultoreſ. Hec·n·opinio
quid agit aliud: niſi ut nulluſ oĩno colat̃:aut roget̃ deuſ? Contra quoſ modo nobiſ
diſputatio nó ẽ inſtituta:ſed cótra eoſ q̃ pro defenſióe eorũ quoſ deoſ putãt xpiane
religiói aduerſant̃. Illi uero q̃ poſitiói ſtellarũ quodãmó decernẽtiũ q̃liſ quiſq̃ ſit &
qd̃ pueniat boni: qd̃ ue mali accidat ex dei uolũtate ſuſpẽdũt:ſi eaſdẽ ſtellaſ putãt
habere hãc ptãrem tradita ſibi a ſũma illiuſ ptãre: ut uolẽteſ iſta decernãt:magnam
celo faciũt iniuriã: in cuiuſ uelut clariſſimo ſeratu ac ſplẽdidiſſima curia opinantur
ſcelera facienda decerni: qualia ſi aliqua terrena ciuitaſ decreuiſſet: genere humano
decernẽte fuerat euertẽda. Quale deĩ iudiciũ de hominũ factiſ deo relinqtur: qbuſ
celeſtiſ neceſſitaſ adhibet̃: cũ dñſ ille ſit & ſiderũ & hominũ? Aut ſi nó dicunt ſtellaſ
accepta qdẽ ptãte a ſũmo deo arbitrio ſuo iſta decernere:ſed in talibuſ neceſſitatibuſ
ingerẽdiſ illiuſ oĩno iuſſa cóplere: ita ne de ipſo ſentiẽdũ ẽ qd̃ indigniſſimũ uiſũ eſt
de ſtellarũ uolũtate ſẽtire? Quod ſi dicunt ſtelle ſignificare potiuſ iſta:q̃ facere:ut q̃ſi
locutio quedã ſit illa poſitio p̃dicenſ futura: nó agẽſ. nó·n·mediocriter doctorũ hoĩm
fuit iſta ſentẽtia.nó quidẽ ita ſolẽt loq̃ mathematici:ut uerbi gratia dicant· Marſ ita
poſituſ homicidã ſignificat: ſed homicidã nó facit. Veruntñ ut cócedamuſ nó eoſ ut
debẽt loqui: & a philoſophiſ accipere oportere ſermóiſ regulã:ad ea p̃nuntiãda: que
in ſiderũ poſitióe reperire ſe putãt: qd̃ ſit de quo nihil unq̃ dicere potuerũt: cur in uita
geminorũ:in actióibuſ & in euẽtiſ:in p̃feſſióibuſ artibuſ:bonoribuſ ceteriſq̃ rebuſ ad
humanã uitã p̃tinẽtibuſ:atq̃ in ipa morte ſit plerũq̃ tãta diuerſitaſ:ut ſimilioreſ eiſ
ſint q̃tũ ad hec attinet:multi extranei:q̃ ipſi inter ſe gemini:p exiguo tpiſ interuallo
in naſcẽdo ſeparati: in cóceptu aũt per unũ cócubitũ uno etiam momento ſeminati.

❧ De geminorum ſimili: diſſimiliq; ualitudine.　　　C. ii.

Icero dicit Hippocratẽ nobiliſſimũ medicũ ſcriptũ reliqſſe:quoſdã fr̃eſ cũ ſimul
egrotare cepiſſent:& eorum morbuſ eodẽ tẽpore ingraueſceret:eodẽ leuaretur

Xiſtunt eedem corone circa Lunam & circa nobilia aſtra celo quoq̃ inherētia
Circa ſolem arcuſ apparuit.L. Opinio.iii.Q. Fabio.ii.Coſſ. Orbiſ : L.
Portio.M.Acilio.

CAP.XXX.De Circuliſ repentiniſ.

Circuluſ rubri coloriſ. L. Iulio. P. Rutilio. Coſſ. Fiunt prodigioſi & longi/
oreſ ſoliſ defectuſ : qualiſ occiſo Dictatore Ceſare & Antoniano bello totiuſ
pene anni pallore continuo.

CAP.XXXI.De Pluribuſ Solibuſ.

T rurſuſ ſoleſ pluref cernuntur : nec ſupra ipſum nec infra ſe: ſed ex obliquo.
nunq̃ iuxta:nec contra terram:nec noctu:ſed aut oriente aut occidēte. Semel
& meridie conſpecti in Boſphoro produntur.qui ab matutino tempore durauerunt in
occaſum. Trinoſ ſoleſ & antiq̃ ſepiuſ uidere. Sicut S P. Poſtumio.Q. Minutio.Q.
Martio.M. Portio.M.Antonio.P. Dolobella.&.M. Lepido.L. Planco Coſſ.
Et noſtra etaſ uidit Diuo Claudio principe conſulatu eiuſ Cornelio Orfito Collega.
Plureſ ſimul q̃m treſ uiſi ad hoc eui nunq̃ produntur.

CAP.XXXII.De Pluribuſ Luniſ.

Lune quoq̃ trine : ut Cn. Domitio. C.F.L. Annio Coſſ.apparuere:quoſ
pleriq̃ appellauerunt Soleſ nocturnoſ.

CAP.XXXIII.Dieſ luce nocte apparere.

Vmen de celo noctu uiſum eſt.C. Cecilio.Cn. Papyrio Coſſ. Et ſepe aliaſ :
ut diei ſpecieſ noctu luceret.

CAP.XXXIIII.Clipei ardenteſ.

Lipeuſ ardenſ ab occaſu ad ortum ſcintillanſ tranſcurrit Soliſ occaſum.L.
Valerio : C. Mario Coſſ.

CAP.XXXV.Oſtentum cæli.

Cintillam e ſtella cadere & augeri terre appropinquantem : ac poſtq̃ in Lune
magnitudinem facta ſit:illuxiſſe ceu nubilo die. dein cum in celum ſe recaperet
lampadem factam ſemel unq̃ proditor.Cn. Octauio.C. Scribonio Coſſ. Vidit hoc
Liciniuſ Sillanuſ Proconful cum comitatu ſuo.

CAP.XXXVI.De Diſcurſu ſtellarum.

Ieri uidetur & diſcurſuſ ſtellarum nunq̃ temere : ut non ex ea parte cruceſ uēti

48 PLINIUS SECUNDUS, GAIUS (PLINY THE ELDER). Natu-
ralis Historia.

Rome, Conradus Sweynheym and Arnoldus Pannartz, 7 May 1473

Thick folio (382 × 270 mm.). Roman type. 46 lines. [401] ff., including the
last blank (lacking the first blank). Capital spaces, with some initials in the
first half of the second book supplied in red, blue and gold; headings of
books 1 and 2 in gold. Late 18th-century English red morocco, gilt-ruled
borders, gilt inside dentelles, back richly gilt, g.e.; by Richard Weir. From
the libraries of Count MacCarthy-Reagh (his sale, 1815/17, no. 1706; of
Henry Drury (his sale, 1827, no. 3456), with his bibliographical notes on
the fly-leaf; of Henry Howard, Duke of Norfolk; of Jorge de Beristayn,
with his notes and his bookplate; and of Harrison D. Horblit, with his
bookplate.

Magnificent copy of the rare last book produced by the famous press of Sweynheym and Pannartz, the first printers in Italy.

Fourth edition of this remarkable encyclopaedia of the ancient world, the major source for most mediaeval knowledge. Divided into thirty-seven books, it represents a compilation of some twenty thousand notices excerpted by Pliny from about two thousand works in all fields of sciences and humanities known in the first century.

An unusually fresh and wide-margined copy, in a superb binding, and with a most distinguished provenance.

H 13090; BMC IV, 17; Goff P-789 (only 2 copies in U.S.); IGI 7881; Klebs 786.4; cf. Ramsden in *BC* 2 (1953), 247-57, on Wier and MacCarthy.

FIRST ROMAN MEDICAL INCUNABLE

49 CAPELLUTUS, ROLANDUS. Tractatus de curatione pestiferorum apostematum.

Rome, Ulrich Han, [c. 1475]

4to (238 × 171 mm.). [6]ff., uncut. Gold-tooled vellum.

First edition, first issue of the first medical incunable to be printed in Rome, and one of the first printed works on the plague, of great rarity. Rolando Capelluti (1430-after 1480) studied medicine at Parma and returned to the city in 1468 upon the outbreak of plague. There he helped to minimize the contagion and administer to the stricken. On the basis of this experience he composed the present treatise, found in two manuscript versions: one abbreviated, the other longer version printed here. This edition was published within three years of the first printed work on the plague.

GW 6017 (recording only 5 copies); Hain 4373; Pell-Pol 3226; IGI 2428; Osler (IM) 81; Klebs 248.1; Klebs-Sudhoff, *Die ersten gedruckten Pestschriften* (1926) no. 36 and pl. XVIII; not in BMC or Goff.

BEAUTIFULLY ILLUMINATED IN A FINE CONTEMPORARY BINDING

50 LEO I (POPE). – ANDREAS, JOHANNES, *ed.* [Sermones et Opusculae.]

[Rome, Joannes Philippus de Lignamine, 1470-1471]

Small folio (281 × 195 mm.). Roman type. 35 lines. [158] ff. (of 160, lacking first and last blanks, wormholes in first few leaves generally confined to lower margin). Opening page with 7-line initial "L" in burnished gold on illuminated ground, attached to a full border of white foliate interlace on a blue, purple, green and burnished-gold ground (shaved at top and bot-

¶ LECTIO SANCTI EVANGELII SECVNDVM IOHANNEM.

IN illo tempore Aſſumpſit Ieſus Petrum Iacobum & Iohanne fratre eius & duxit eos in montem excelſum ſeorſum. Et reliqua. ¶ OMELIA SANCTI LEONIS PAPE

DE TRANSFIGVRATIONE DOMINI.

EVangelica dilectiſſimi lectio quę per aures corporis interiorem mentium nřaꝛ pulſauit auditu ad magni ſacramenti nos intelligentiā uocat:quā aſpirāte gratia dei facilius aſſequemur:ſi cōſideratione nřam ad ea quę paulo ſupius ſunt narrata referamus. Saluator eim bꭒani generis Ieſus Chriſtus condens eā fidē quę & impios ad iuſticiā & mortuos reuocat ad uitam:ad boc diſcipulos ſuos doctrię monitis & opeꝛ miraculis imbuebat:ut idē Chriſtus & uni/ genitus dei & hominis filius crederet. Nā unū borum ſine altero nō ꝓderat ad ſalutē:& ꝗqualis erat periculi dominū Ieſum Chriſtū aut deū tm̄mō ſine hōie aut ſine deo ſolum bꭒēm credidiſſe cū utrūꝗ eſſet pariter cōfitendū:ꝗa ſicut deo uera bꭒanitas ita hōi inerat uera diuinitas. Ad cōfir/ mādū ergo buius fidei ſaluberrimā cognitōne : interroga/ uerat diſcipulos ſuos dn̄s:Inter diuerſas alioꝛ opiniones: quid ipſi de eo crederēt:qꝗdue ſentirent. ubi Petrus Apl̄s ꝑ reuelatione ſūmi pr̄ꝭ corpea ſupans & bꭒana trāſcēdēs uidit mētis oculis filiū dei uiui & cōfeſſus ē gloriā deitatis: quia nō ad ſola reſpexit carnis ſubſtātiā & ſanguis tantūꝗ in bac fidei ſublimitate cōplacuit:ut beatitudinis felicitate donatus ſacrā inuiolabilis petrę accipet firmitatē.ſuꝑ quā fundata eccl̄ia portis inferi & mortis legibus p̄ualeret.nec in ſoluendis & ligandis quorūcūꝗ cauſis aliud ratū eſſet in cęlis ꝙ quod Petri ſediſſet arbitrio.Hac autem dilectiſſimi laude intelligentię celſitudo inſtruenda erat de inferioris ſubſtātię ſacrameto:ne apoſtolica fides ad gloriā cōfitēdę in Chriſto deitatis euecta infirmitatis nřę redemptionem indignā impaſſibili deo atꝗ incongruā iudicaret.& ita iam tom); two 6-line initials in purple or blue and green with green or purple foliate infill on a burnished gold ground, with illumination extending into the margin (ff. 67, 127ᵛ); many 2-line initials in red or blue with red or purple penwork infilling and marginal extenders. Contemporary South German richly blind-tooled pigskin over oak boards, one large frame with central panel filled with 3 floral stamps and 2 sizes of fleurs-de-lys, brass clasps and catches (a few mends to spine); pastedowns of incunable leaves. A few contemporary marginalia. From the libraries of Sidney Hellman Ehrman, with his signature in his lithographed bookplate; and of William L. Thomas with his signature on a slip pasted on the front flyleaf.

An exquisite piece of early printing from Lignamine's first press, the third printing establishment at Rome. This is the second edition of this work, reprinted with the preface from Sweynheym and Pannartz's edition of 1470. It is the third book printed by Lignamine, a native of Messina and papal physician.

The volume is of special interest for the chapter headings some of which are stamped by hand in large type, others filled in manuscript, and some left blank.

H 10010; BMC IV, 29; Goff L-131; Pell 7125; BNIC L-112; IGI 5723.

51 MAROLDUS, MARCUS. Or[ati]o de epiphania.

[Rome, Bartholomaeus Guldinbeck, c. 1485]

8 vo (205 × 142 mm.). Gothic type. 35 lines. [11] pp. unsigned. Modern boards.

Second edition of this oration delivered before Sixtus IV in January 1475 and first printed about that date by J. Gensberg. Little is known of the author except that he was a Neapolitan (d. 1495), and held the office of official papal theologian.

The types of Bartholomaeus Guldinbeck and those of Wendelinus de Wila are hard to distinguish in unsigned and undated editions and Proctor grouped them all under the present printer.

This little oration of Maroldus is quite rare, there being no copy in BMC, including Supplement, or in Polain, IGI, or IDL. A clean, wide-margined copy.

C-3884; Goff M-278 (only 1 copy); BNIC M-139; Pell-Pol 7663; Proctor 3595 (Bodleian only); Hubay, *Würzburg* 1402.

52 PTOLEMAEUS, CLAUDIUS. Cosmographia.

Rome, Arnold Buckinck, 10 October 1478

Folio (395 × 250 mm.). Roman type. 50 lines. 2 cols. [66] ff. (of 70, lacking

3 printed ff. – a₂ e₁ e₈ – which are supplied in facsimile, and 1 blank; 6 ff. renewed in lower margins; some thumbing and spotting on first and last leaves of text and small hole on first leaf affecting one letter of text). Initials supplied throughout in red or blue. With 27 double folio engraved maps on 54 ff. (some browning on first map, the world, and a small wormhole at edge of print; three other maps – Quinta Europae, Sexta Europae, and Undecima Asiae – mended in margins just touching print; few scattered wormholes on last four maps). Woodcut diagrams in text, some explanatory words in ms. in diagrams and a few other entries in ms., which are in the same handwriting in all copies and were undoubtedly written in the printer's office. 18th-century Spanish mottled calf, gilt back. With ms. exlibris of Petrus Servius, physician (17th-century); and Hernando Affonso Giralo (19th-century).

One of the great classics of science and art. It is the fourth earliest book to contain engravings, but it seems certain that those of this present Rome edition were in preparation before the preceding Bologna edition of the same year, and possibly even before the two earliest books, the Mansion *Boccaccio* of 1476 and the Bettini *Monte Sancto* of 1477. The engravings are generally considered to have been made by Conrad Sweynheym or under his immediate supervision. (See Scholderer, *Fifty Essays*, p. 203.)

A statement regarding Sweynheym in the dedicatory letter of this volume says that he had worked on the preparation of the engravings for three years before his death (the date is not given). It would appear that he began work on the Ptolemy after the dissolution of his partnership with Pannartz in 1473. Their last joint work appeared on 7 May 1473, and as the contract between Crivelli, the engraver, and his backers for producing the Bologna Ptolemy (issued 23 June 1477) was signed only in 1474, it seems likely that work on the Rome edition began earlier than that on the Bologna.

A. M. Hind refers to the "excellent printing (which) seconds the quality of the engraving in the Roman Ptolemy", and the impressions are very sharp and dark. The wiping of the plates was not carried out to the bottom edge (the wiping is invariably from top to bottom) and this has left irregularly darkened areas in the lower margins. This occurs in all copies, however. Also, according to Hind, "The engraver of the Roman edition is far more skillful as an engraver (than Crivelli). He does not indulge his pictorial fancy, for the Map of the World is without the wind-faces common to this subject. But in the symbolic representation of natural features, forests and mountains, he shows a practiced hand, and nothing can exceed the purity and precision of his engravings of both maps and lettering".

The Petrus Servius whose exlibris is on the title-page is probably the Roman physician (d. 1634), noted also as a scholar of classical antiquities.

HC 13537; BMC IV, 78; Goff P-1083; Sander 5975; Sabin 66470; IGI 8182; Klebs 812.3; Hind, *Early Ital. Engr.*, I, p. 290.

53 PIUS II [AENEAS SILVIUS PICCOLOMINI]. Tractatulus de duobus se invicem amantibus [Historia de duobus amantibus Euryalo et Lucretia].

[Rome, Stephan Plannck], 15 July 1485

8vo. Gothic type. 33 lines. [25] ff. (lacking final blank leaf, a few stains, some inner margins strengthened, some repaired tears). Added are [11] ff. of 17th-century manuscript notes on the text, the author and his other works. Crushed burgundy morocco, gold inner rules, gold-stamped title on spine, g.e., by Leighton. From the library of Sidney Graves Hamilton, with his engraved armorial bookplate.

An early edition of this celebrated love story written by Aeneas Silvius Piccolomini, the future pope; it is one of the first novels in the modern sense and is based upon a true story, an amorous adventure of the German Chancellor Gaspar Schlick, a friend of Piccolomini's, with a Siennese lady. First published c. 1473, it was often reprinted and translated in the 15th century. The text is preceded by 3 letters of Piccolomini, including one to Gaspar Schlick.

An early 17th-century owner has added some learned notes on the author, his text, and extracts from his other works on the baths of Baden, and on Vienna.

H 234; Goff P-681; Pell 163; IGI 7806.

PRINTED ON VELLUM AND ILLUMINATED
THE LOMENIE-MACCARTHY-SPENCER COPY

54 AUGUSTINUS, AURELIUS. De civitate dei.

Venice, Johannes & Vindelinus de Spira, 1470

On vellum. Folio (372 × 250 mm.). Roman type. 50 lines. Table, 2 cols. [271] ff. of (274, lacking the three blanks as usual; natural vellum flaws, some repaired; 2 or 3 worm-punctures in first 14 ff., one occasionally touching a letter of text; few minuscule worm-punctures, mostly marginal, in last 20 ff.). Large 14-line opening text initial "I" and another of 9 lines, plus 21 8-line initials, all in burnished gold on grounds of red, blue, and green, patterned with tiny white triple dots, white leafy scrolls in centers; small 2-line initials and paragraph marks supplied in red or blue; chapter headings supplied in light red on first 9 text leaves (painted coat of arms almost completely erased from lower margin of first text leaf). Early 19th-century English straight-grained dark blue morocco, panelled sides with gilt palmettes at outer angles, at the inner ones solid and pointillé tools of quatrefoils, small circles, and leafy sprays on a dotted ground; back richly gilt in similar style, g.e.; John Rylands monogram added later in center of upper cover. In a half-morocco drop-box. From the libraries of Etienne Charles de Lo-ménie de Brienne, Cardinal Archbishop of Toulouse and of Sens (his sale, Paris, March 1792, Laire, *Ind.*, I, p. 217, no. 2); of Count Justin MacCarthy Reagh (his sale, Paris, 1817, lot 543); of George John, Earl Spencer (not the copy described by Dibdin in *Bibliotheca Spenceriana*), with his leather label; and of the John Rylands library, with its release label.

Superb copy on vellum of the fourth book printed at Venice by the proto-typographer who was the first to use a pure roman type. The colophon to this book represents an important source of information in the history of printing since it states that Johannes de Spira produced one hundred copies of Pliny and the same number of Cicero within the extraordinary time of less than three months, and had died when the present work was in progress, leaving its completion to his brother Vindelinus whose name appears here for the first time. Curiously, it does not mention the second edition of three hundred copies of Cicero also printed in 1469.

The illumination is very fresh and bright and the volume is generally in very fine condition. Only nine copies on vellum are known of one of the greatest books of Christianity.

GW 2877; H 2048; BMC V, 153; Goff A-1233 (1 copy on vellum); Pell 1547; Pol 357; IGI 969; IDL 490; Van Praet (*Roi*) I, 275–76 and V, 366; Dibdin IV, 932 describing another copy, not on vellum.

54 Augustinus on vellum

55 APPIANUS. – DECEMBRIUS, PETRUS CANDIDUS, *trans.*
Historia Romana [de civilibus Romanorum bellis].

[Venice], Vindelinus de Spira, 1472

Small folio (308 × 198 mm.). Roman type. 41 lines. [146] ff. (of 148, lacking the first and last blanks, 7 ff. lightly dampstained in upper portion, some worm-punctures in first and last few ff., contemporary marginalia erased). Three-quarter woodcut border on f. 3 illuminated with colored washes in blue, purple, pale green and silver (oxidized, some loss of pigment due to damp); 7- and 6-line woodcut initials similarly illuminated; f.2 with capital spaces with guide letters filled in by the rubricator in red and blue.

(*Bound with*:) PIASECKI, PAUL. Chronica gestorum in europa sin-gularium.

Cracow, Franciscus Caesarius, 1645

[4], 619, [1] pp. (lacking the portrait and 10 ff. of Index). Woodcut title vignette and initials. 18th-century calf (worn), back gilt.

First edition of any part of Appianus' *Historia Romana* of which only eleven books and some fragments of the original twenty-four are extant. This edition includes the Roman civil wars of books 13-17. The original Greek text appeared only in 1551.

Especially remarkable is the presence of the woodcut border and woodcut initials which are found only in some copies. These, it has been suggested, were used by the illuminator to increase his production, and are found in various editions by various printers.

Bound in front is the first edition of a history of Poland in the late sixteenth and early seventeenth century by the bishop of Przemsyl, Pawel Piasecki (1579-1649).

I: GW 2293; H 1306; BMC V, 160; Goff A-931; Pell 914; IGI 766; IDL 380; Essling I, no. 220; Goff, "Illuminated woodcut borders and initials in early Venetian books (1469-1475)", *GJ* (1962), pp. 380–389 with reproduction fig. 4.

II: Estreicher XXIV, 230; Hoskins, *Early and Rare Polonica* (1973), no. 770.

THE FIRST PRINTING OF HOMER
A UNIQUE EXAMPLE OF "POUNCING" IN A PRINTED BOOK

56 MACROBIUS, AURELIUS THEODOSIUS. Somnium Scipi-onis. Saturnalia.

Venice, Nicolaus Jenson, 1472

Folio (314 × 211 mm.). Roman and Greek type. 40 lines. [163] leaves, see

collation note below (a few marginal stains; 5 tiny marginal repairs; occasional old marginalia and old ms. exlibris on blank f. 143ᵛ). 10 large initials
in various colors with interlaced yellow ornaments, in the style of the 12th
century; 5 of them perforated with many tiny pinholes (see below); numerous
smaller initials in red; spaces left for diagrams and occasionally for Greek
quotations. Modern richly blind-tooled calf in the style of the 15th century,
gilt-stamped initials J E H[odgkin] in front center panel, inside gilt border,
gauffered gilt edges. From the libraries of Milo Symnor, with his bibliographical note, dated 12 May 1664, beneath the colophon; of John Eliot
Hodgkin (his sale, 1914, no. 952), with his two bookplates and his "Annotatio" slip with ms. notes; and of Harrison D. Horblit.

Editio princeps and a magnificent specimen of Jenson's typography, displaying both his elegant Greek and roman fonts.

The *Saturnalia* are notable for containing the first printed texts of Homer
(about 400 lines in Greek) and Lucretius (about 120 lines), in addition to passages from Aristotle, Plato, Euripides, Pindar and others, printed here in Greek
for the first time. The *Somnium*, a commentary on Cicero's "Dream of Scipio",
offers much information on the Neoplatonic views of geography and astronomy, including the so-called "Oceanic Theory" and the "Doctrine of the Four
Worlds".

This copy is also highly interesting for being a rare example of an old copying
technique known as "pouncing": The outlines of the figure to be copied, in this
case ornamental initials, were marked by very closely spaced pin-holes and a
piece of paper was placed under the original. Then fine powdered charcoal was
poured into a small porous linen or muslin bag and rubbed over the original;
some powder particles were forced through the holes and thus copied the outlines
of the paper underneath. (This procedure inevitably left some powder smudges
on the original.) The present copy seems to be the only known printed book to have
been subjected to this technique; all other recorded instances of pouncing are
found in works of art (especially designs to be transferred to frescoes) or in illuminated manuscripts.

A highly desirable copy of a significant book in both literature and typography.

Collation note: The present copy collates (a8 b12 c–m6.10 n8 o–t10.6 v10–3),
differing from the collation given in BMC. Apparently 3 blank leaves at the end
are not present; the first quire of this copy does not call for an initial blank. The
text is complete. Back fly-leaf with an extensive bibliographical note in a 19th-
century hand.

HC 10426; BMC V, 172; Goff M-8; IGI 5923; Klebs 638.1; Hodgkin, *Rariora*, II,
88–90 (this copy); About pouncing see S. A. Ives and H. Lehmann-Haupt, *An English
13th century Bestiary* (1942), 35 ff.

57 DIONYSIUS PERIEGETES. – BECCARIA, ANTONIO, *trans.*
De situ orbis.

Venice, Franciscus Renner de Heilbronn, 1478

Small 4to (186 × 142 mm.). Roman type. 26 lines. [36] ff. (tear in f. e₁ repaired, light dampstain in upper outer corner). Title printed in red; fine ornamental woodcut initials. 18th-century brown boards with calf back and corners (foot of spine split). From the library of the abbey of Steingaden, Bavaria, with its ms. exlibris on first page; and of Sir Thomas Phillipps with his pencilled "MHC".

Second edition of Dionysius Periegetes' only surviving work, a description of the world, in 1187 hexameters. The author flourished some time in the first or second century, probably under Domitian (81-96 A.D.), and his poem exerted great influence during the Middle Ages.

The translation into Latin was done by the humanist Antonio Beccaria (c. 1400-1474), who was renowned for his skill and knowledge of Latin and Greek. At the invitation of the Duke of Gloucester, he spent some time in England. The book, produced during Franciscus Renner's first year of solo operation, is a most handsome work with printed marginalia and beautiful white-on-black initials.

GW 8427; H 6227; BMC V 195; Goff D-254; Pol 1298; Pell 4294; IDL 1556; IGI 3488; Klebs 340.2.

58 ALCHABITIUS (AL-QABISI). – JOHANNES HISPALENSIS *trans.* Libellus ysagogicus.

Venice, Erhard Ratdolt, 16 January 1482

Small 4to (190 × 143 mm.). Gothic type. 31 lines. [32] ff. With 2 woodcut diagrams and several decorated woodcut initials; heading on first page printed in red. 19th-century decorated flexible boards, in cloth drop-box. Early ms. exlibris of an unidentified Franciscan library, and from the libraries of Gilbert R. Redgrave; and of Harrison D. Horblit, with their bookplates.

Second edition of this tenth-century Arabic introduction to astrology, the author's principal surviving treatise. For all practical purposes, this is the earliest edition available, since the first edition, printed in Mantua in 1473, survives in only very few (institutional) copies, none of them in America.

This copy was owned by Gilbert R. Redgrave, the great bibliographer and Ratdolt scholar, and has his bookplate as well as his bibliographical notes on the insides of both covers (cf. his sale, 1926, no. 10).

GW 843; BMC V 285; Goff A-362; Pell 417; IGI 267; IDL 169; Essling 294; Sander 216; Houzeau-L. 3847; Redgrave, *Ratdolt*, no. 24.

59 JOHANNES DE SACRO BUSTO (SACROBOSCO). Sphaeri-
cum opusculum. (With two tracts by Regiomontanus and Peurbach.).

[Venice], Erhard Ratdolt, 6 July 1482

Small 4to (204 × 147 mm.). Gothic type. 31 lines. [60] leaves. Heading
printed in red. Full-page woodcut of armillary sphere and 39 woodcut
diagrams, 8 of which are colored by a contemporary hand; many ornamental woodcut initials. Modern vellum with beautiful and elaborate hand-
painted signs of the zodiac and floral sprays on both covers; hand-painted
figure of the author (?) accompanied by a little monk, surrounded by a
ribbon with zodiac symbols, in center panel of front cover. From the library
of Harrison D. Horblit.

The first of the beautiful Ratdolt editions of this famous book of mediaeval
astronomy, discussing the theoretical mechanism of the universe. The fine woodcut diagrams are among the earliest woodcuts used for scientific purposes.

This edition also includes the *Disputationes contra Cremonensia* by Regiomontanus and the *Theoricae novae planetarum* by Peurbach.

A magnificent copy in a very special binding.

H 14110; BMC V, 286; Goff J-405; IGI 5343; Essling 258; Sander 6661; Redgrave,
Ratdolt, 27.

FOUR VENETIAN SCIENTIFIC INCUNABULA UNITED

60 JOHANNES DE SACRO BUSTO (SACROBOSCO). Sphaeri-
cum opusculum. (With two tracts by Regiomontanus and Peurbach.).

[Venice], Erhard Ratdolt, 6 July 1482

Small 4to (204 × 149 mm.). Gothic type. 31 lines. [60] ff. Heading printed
in red. Full-page woodcut of armillary sphere and 39 woodcut diagrams,
8 of which are colored by a contemporary hand; many ornamental woodcut initials.

(*Bound with:*) HYGINUS. – SENTINUS, JACOBUS; SANTRIT-
TER, JOHANNES LUCILIUS, *eds.* Poeticon Astronomicon.

Venice, [Erhard Ratdolt], 14 October 1482

Gothic type. 31 lines. [58] ff., the first blank (small stain in lower inner
blank corner). Heading printed in red. 47 very fine woodcut illustrations;
many ornamental woodcut initials.

(*Bound with:*) MELA, POMPONIUS, [Cosmographia.] De situ orbis.

Venice, Franciscus Renner, 1478

Pomponij Mellę Cosmographi de
situ orbis liber primus. Procemium.

Rbis situ dicere aggredior
impeditum opus & facun-
dię minime capax. Cõstat
enim fere gentiũ locorũ q;
nominibus: & eorum per-
plexo satis ordine : quem
persequi longa est magis q̃ benigna materia:
Veꝛ aspici tamen cognosciq; dignissimũ : &
quod si nõ ope ingenij orantis: at ipsa sui con-
templatione pretium operę attendentiũ ab-
soluat. Dicam autem alias plura & exactius:
Nunc autẽ ut quęq; erũt clarissima & strictim
ac primo quidẽ quę sit forma totius: quę ma-
ximę partes. quo singulę modo sint: utq; ha-
bitent expediam. Deinde rursus oras omniũ
& littora ut intra extraq; sunt : atq; ut ea subit
ac circumluit pelagus : additis quę in natura
regionum incolarumq; memoranda sunt. Id
quo facilius sciri possit atq; accipi: paulo altius
summa repetetur.

Mundi ĩ quattuor partes diuisio
Mne igitur hoc quicquid est: cui
mundi cęliq; nomen indidimus:
unũ id est: & uno ãbitu se cũctaq;

a

Roman type. 26 lines. [48] ff. (some lightly stained in lower parts). Chapter headings printed in red; printed marginalia; decorative woodcut initials. (*And with*:) DIONYSIUS PERIEGETES. – BECCARIA, ANTONIUS, *trans*. [Cosmographia]. De situ orbis.

Venice, Franciscus Renner, 1478

Roman type. 26 lines. [35] ff. (of 36, lacking final leaf; last two leaves repaired, affecting text on one). Heading printed in red; printed marginalia; decorative woodcut initials. Pigskin back over wooden boards, metal clasp. From the libraries of Wilhelm Christoph Adelmann, with his ms. exlibris; and of Harrison D. Horblit.

Ad I: This is the first of the beautiful Ratdolt editions of this influential book on the theoretical mechanism of the universe. The fine astronomical diagrams are among the earliest woodcuts used for scientific purposes.

Ad II: The first appearance of an extraordinary series of woodcuts illustrating the constellations and the planets, which was to become the model for similar illustrations throughout the fifteenth and sixteenth centuries. The verses by Sentinus at the end imply that Santritter designed these spirited illustrations. In this copy two of the illustrations are neatly imitated in red pencil on the same page (ff. d8v and e7r). This book is a typical example of Ratdolt's skill applied to both typography and illustration; it must have been extremely popular considering the many reprints.

Ad III: A summary of descriptive geography by the earliest Roman geographer (ca. A.D. 43). A very close reprint of the Ratdolt edition of the same year.

Ad IV: Second edition of this popular poem describing the world. Originally written in Greek in the third century B.C., it exerted a great influence in the Middle Ages in its Latin translations. It contains the first mention of the Huns.

Ad I: H 14110; BMC V, 286; Goff J405; IGI 5343; Essling 248; Sander 6661; Redgrave, *Ratdolt*, 27

Ad II: H 9062; BMC V, 286; Goff H560; Pol 2039; IGI 4959; Essling 285; Sander 3472; Redgrave, *Ratdolt*, 30

Ad III: H 11017; BMC V, 195; Goff M450; Pol 2662; IGI 6343

Ad IV: GW 8427; BMC V 195; Goff D254; Pell 4294; Pol 1298; IGI 3488; Cf. Sarton I, 258.

61 MELA, POMPONIUS. [Cosmographia sive de situ orbis]. Pomponii Mellae Cosmographi Geographia. Prisciani quoque ex dionysio Thessalonicensi de situ orbis interpretatio.

Venice, Erhard Ratdolt, 18 July 1482

Small 4to (192 × 141 mm.). Gothic type. 31 lines. [48] f. (corners of 4 leaves lightly waterstained). With full-page woodcut map (supplied from another copy, top and right-hand margins shaved), 2 large and 11 smaller floral woodcut initials; heading of f. A₂ printed in red. Modern brown calf, blind-ruled. Old ms. exlibris "Citta della S: Francisci" and shelf-mark on f. A₂; bookplate of José M. Rodriquez.

First edition with the map of the most popular compendium of geography printed in the fifteenth century.

The modified Ptolemaic map of the world (Europe, Asia, North Africa), for which this edition is notable, is a very early example of true chiaroscuro printing. It is interesting to note that the source of the Nile on this map is shown to be two lakes which correspond in location with those now known to be the Albert and Victoria Nyanza, demonstrating that their existence was surmised if not actually known many centuries before their re-discovery.

Church 1; Streeter 1; JCB (Bartlett) 2; H 11019; BMC V, 286; Goff M-452; Pol 2663; IGI 6344; Essling 274; Sander 4485; Redgrave, *Ratdolt* 28.

62 PETRARCA, FRANCESCO. – LAPINI DA SIENA, BERNARDO, *comm.* Triumphi.

Venice, Theodorus de Reynsburch and Reynaldus de Novimagio, 6 February 1478

Small folio (268 × 184 mm.). Gothic type. 51 lines. 194 ff. (of 196; lacking the first blank and f. ee₄. First third of book stained, some leaves soiled, last six leaves with two small holes and marginal worming; old marginalia.). 18th-century half calf (corners rubbed). Bookplate of M. Costa.

This famous extensive commentary, surrounding the broken-up Petrarca text, was printed by one of the leading early Venetian presses in its first year. It is one of the very few incunabula having both I and J as signature marks.

A companion volume, containing the Sonetti and Canzoni, was published on 30 March 1478.

H 12767; BMC V, 254; Goff P-381; IGI 7545.

63 SERAPION THE YOUNGER. – JANUENSIS, SIMON, *trans.*
Liber aggregatus in medicinis simplicibus.

Venice, Reynaldus de Novimagio, 8 June 1479

Folio (290 × 203 mm.). Gothic type. 53 lines. 2 cols. [136] ff. including 3 blank; ff. g₃ and g₈ torn, loss of text replaced by old pen-and-ink facsimile; a few small stains). Several large decorative initials in red and blue penwork; numerous smaller ones supplied in red or blue. 19th-century half calf. From the library of John Lawson, M.D., with his ms. exlibris on pastedown and notes on fly-leaf; donated by him to Sion College, 1705, with its stamped, printed, and engraved exlibris.

An Arabic treatise on animal, vegetable and mineral medicinal substances, translated into Latin by Simon of Genoa and Abraham ben Shem Tob. The work was probably written in the twelfth century, and it was translated in the second half of the thirteenth century. Practically nothing is known about Serapion (Ibn Sarabi); he is not, however, the ninth-century Arabic physician, nor the even earlier Alexandrian writer. Only a part of the text is now known in the Arabic; there is an extant Hebrew version.

As with all such medical works, many of the chapters have a subsidiary gastronomical interest, as they describe common foods and drink, such as grapes (f. 23), wine (f. 24), sugar (f. 28), sesame (f. 35), chestnut (f. 38), etc.

HC 14692; BMC V 255; Goff S-468; Klebs 913.2; See also Sarton, II, 229.

64 Boccaccio (*reduced*)

THE FIRST ILLUSTRATED ITALIAN DECAMERON

64 BOCCACCIO, GIOVANNI. Decamerone o ver cento novelle.

Venice, Johannes & Gregorius de Gregoriis, 20 June 1492

Folio (405 × 212 mm.). Roman type. 58-59 lines. 2 cols. [4], 137 = [141] ff. (of 144, lacking 2 blanks and the one-line title, the latter supplied in facsimile; 11 ff., including large cut with border, supplied from another copy;

fore margin of *₅ renewed; some worm-punctures in first 3 quires, sometimes touching a letter; small tear repaired on a₂ and on n₅; occasional minor thumbing or spotting). Large woodcut within historiated architectural woodcut border, 2 other large woodcuts (c. 106 × 121 mm.), one appearing seven times, the other three; 100 small column-width cuts, 2 small author-portraits (the 3 woodcuts on b₁, s₁, and u₃ are supplied from the 1498 edition); large woodcut printer's mark on verso of last leaf. English 19th-century tan calf, with double gilt rules, small flower sprays on back, with supralibros of the Royal Society at the base of the spine. In a half-morocco drop-box. From the libraries of Henry Howard, Duke of Norfolk (1628–1684); with his donation stamp on f.5v to the Royal Society (its sale, Sotheby, 4 May 1925, lot 27); of George W. Jones? (his sale, Sotheby, 1 July 1936, lot 77?); of Martin Bodmer; and of Otto Schäfer, with his monogram stamp on rear pastedown.

The first illustrated Italian edition of the Decameron and the first to contain the *Vita*. The delightful illustrations by the Venetian "Popular Designer" the "Master of the Malermi Bible" (1490) are of great interest for their depictions of costume, customs, and interiors of Florentine life in the last decade of the fifteenth century. The large illustration on the first text leaf shows the whole company seated in an arbor in a garden, each identified by name; the other two large cuts show the "king" or "queen" chosen each day to preside over the storytelling, and the company with a lute-player. This copy obviously fell victim to censorship, since all the supplied leaves and cuts depict either nudity or couples making love. In this copy, as in two others known, the cut on f. 37v is repeated on f. 73, probably due to a damaged block, and (as in all known copies) the woodcuts for novellas IX, 6 and IX, 9 are interchanged. Thirteen of the small cuts have a tiny "b" in one of the lower corners, perhaps the signature of the woodcutter. Some of the cuts exhibit a charming naiveté and slightly licentious wit, while others - notably the larger ones - have an air of classical grace.

Although it would seem at first sight that the provenance of this copy can be traded from the Duke of Norfolk to Otto Schäfer, there appears to be a discrepancy between the copy described in the Jones sale catalogue and the present one. There it was noted that there was "the numeral cut and headline touched on fol. 80, margin of fol. 5 renewed". The present copy does indeed have the fore margin of f. 5 renewed, but there is no trace of damage or repair to f. 80. It seems unlikely that there would be another copy otherwise agreeing with ours, but it is possible that other copies were mutilated to remove the offending woodcuts.

Only nine complete copies are recorded, and five incomplete of this extremely rare Italian illustrated book, this and the present Schäfer copy being the only ones in private hands.

GW 4449; HC 3277b; Goff B-728; Pell 2442; IGI 1777; Essling 640 (with 7 illus.); Sander 1060 (13 illus.); Schäfer Cat., 62 (this copy); Bodmer, *Choix d'incunables illustrés* (1954), p. 33 (this copy); Hind, p. 477 et seq.

65 JOHANNES DE SACRO BUSTO (SACROBOSCO). Sphaera mundi. (With two other tracts by Regiomontanus and Peurbach.)

Venice, [Bonetus Locatellus] for Octavianus Scotus, 4 October 1490

4to (216 × 160 mm.). Roman type. 41 lines. [48] ff., (ff.d$_1$ and d$_8$ reversed in binding; last leaf on stub and with marginal holes; a few margins lightly stained; some old marginalia). One full-page woodcut of Urania, Astronomia, Ptolemy on verso of title, and numerous woodcut diagrams, 7 of which are stencilled in 2 or 3 colors; woodcut publisher's device at end, printed in red; two sets of ornamental woodcut initials. Boards. From the libraries of Carl J. Ulman, with his bookplate; and of Harrison D. Horblit.

The fine full-page woodcut and the diagrams were designed by J. L. Santritter and cut by Hieronymus de Sanctis and employed before in their 1488 edition of this book. An early example of color stencilling.

The text of this popular mediaeval astronomical work is based on the Ratdolt edition of 1485. Appended are the *Disputationes contra Cremonensia* by Regiomontanus and the *Theoricae novae planetarum* by Peurbach.

H 14113; BMC V, 438; Goff J-409; Pol 2303; IGI 5346; Essling 261; Sander 6664; IDL 2704.

66 JOHANNES DE SACRO BUSTO (SACROBOSCO). Sphaera mundi. (With two other tracts by Regiomontanus and Peurbach.).

Venice, Guilelmus Anima Mia, Tridinensis, 14 January 1491

Small 4to (194 × 146 mm.). Roman type. 42 lines. [48] leaves. One full-page woodcut of Urania, Astronomia, Ptolemy on verso of title, and numerous woodcut diagrams, 7 of which are stencilled in 2 or 3 colors; ornamental woodcut initials. Vellum. From the library of Harrison D. Horblit, with his bookplate.

This is a page-for-page reprint of Locatellus' edition of 1490, employing the diagrams designed and cut by Santritter and Hieronymus de Sanctis. The text is based on the Ratdolt edition of 1485 and had Regiomontanus' *Disputationes* and Peurbach's *Theoricae novae* appended.

H 14114; BMC V 412; Goff J-410; Pol 2304; IGI 5347; Essling 262; Sander 6665.

67 MELA, POMPONIUS. – BARBARUS, HERMOLAUS, *ed.* [Cosmographia sive] de situ orbis.

[Venice, Christophorus de Pensis, de Mandello, after 1493?]

Small 4to (210 × 158 mm.). Roman type. 27 lines. [38] ff. (portions waterstained); contemporary marginalia. Many ornamental woodcut initials. Wrappers. From the library of Harrison D. Horblit, with bookplate.

Unusually wide-margined copy, with some edges uncut, of this popular geographical compendium.

It is interesting to note that BMC mentions only capital spaces with guide letters, whereas the present copy displays many beautiful ornamental woodcut initials, sometimes incorporating little figures.

H 11013; BMC V, 476; Goff M-453; IGI 6346; Klebs 675.8; IDL 377.

68 PRISCIANUS. – BROGNOLUS, BENEDICTUS, *ed.*; AIGRE, JOANNES DE, *comm.* Opera.

Venice, Philippus Pincius, 20 June 1492

Folio (321 × 215 mm.). Roman, with some Greek, types. 46 lines text when full page, 60 lines commentary. 313 (i.e. 307) ff. (title being last leaf of last quire as in BMC copy; lacking first blank; few light marginal stains at beginning and end). 5 illuminated initials in colors and gold; illuminated ecclesiastical coat of arms of the Potier family in lower margin of opening text leaf. Contemporary Cambridge binding by W.G. (or G.W), blind-tooled dark brown calf over wooden boards; intersecting frame extending to edges and back, the central panel divided by diagonal fillets into lozenge and triangular compartments; these compartments with four different single stamps of a shield with W.G., lily in lozenge, fleur-de-lys in circle, and fleur-de-lys cruciform lozenge; within the dividing fillets of the intersecting frame an acorn border stamp (rebacked, original backstrip laid down); clasps and metal catches (clasps repaired); front pastedown of vellum leaf from a 13th-century legal manuscript. Date of 1551 on front flyleaf; later inscription "At the Fox and Crown in Barbakin (Barbican) for Mr. Good-win." Some early marginalia in a fine delicate hand.

A Venetian edition of Priscianus, the celebrated Latin grammarian of the fifth century. Most of the book consists of his systematic exposition of Latin grammar, dedicated to Julian, consul and patrician, divided into eighteen books. This was used as the standard Latin grammar until the fifteenth century and is still useful for its extracts from many classical authors whose works are now lost. At the end of this volume are several of the author's short works such as his treatise on weights and measures, on the metres of Terence, and his translation of Dionysius's *Periegesis*, into Latin hexameters as *De orbis situ*, or a geographical survey of the world.

A very handsome example of English binding, c. 1500. The Mr. Goodwin referred to in the inscription may be Thomas Goodwin (1600-1680), English divine, who was known to have an extensive library, part of which was destroyed in the Great Fire of London, 1666.

HC 13362; BMC V, 493; Goff P-969; IGI 8054; Klebs 806.10; Hobson, *Cambridge* pp. 46/7, pl. XV, nos. 33–37; Hobson, *Shrewsbury*, pp. 58/9; Oldham, *Blind-Stamped Bindings*, pp. 16/7, pl. X, nos. 20–24.

69 MUNDINUS (MONDINO DEI LUZZI). – GEORGIUS, VIN-CENTIUS, *ed*. Anathomia. [Anatomia corporis humani]

Venice, Bernardinus Venetus, de Vitalibus for Hieronymus de Durantibus, 20 Feb. 1494 [–1495]

4to (207 × 150 mm.). Gothic type. 43 lines. 24 ff. (some minor staining). Boards. With ms. exlibris (17th century) of Jo. Ant. Balbani.

One of the most influential mediaeval medical texts. Mondino (1275-1326) was one of the earliest post-classical anatomists to dissect the human body. He was professor at Bologna, and was physician to Robert d'Anjou, King of Naples. "This work was the most popular text-book during the period 1470-1530. After the invention of printing it became a kind of student's compend, and passed through 39 separate editions and translations . . . Mundinus' work at Bologna was continued by his pupil Niccolo Bertuccio (d. 1347) who taught Guy de Chauliac. After this time dissection gained a firmer foothold as a mode of in-struction". (Garrison).

The Mondino text was one of those printed in the famous collection, *Fasci-culus Medicinae* (ed. Ketham), which was issued with splendid Venetian wood-cuts of dissections. This is the seventh edition of this text.

HR 11638; Goff M-8757; Pol 2794; IGI 5915; Klebs 688.7; not in BMC.

70 ALBERTUS OF SAXONY. Questiones subtilissime in libros de caelo et mundo.

Venice, Otinus de Luna, Papiensis, 9 June 1497

Folio (284 × 198 mm.). Gothic type. 72 lines. 2 cols. [51] ff. (of 52. final blank not present; light dampstaining in first third of book). 15th-century vellum ms. leaf over boards (some worming). Ownership inscription on last leaf, dated 1497, crossed out and one of 1548 substituted.

Albert of Saxony (c. 1316-1390) was born in Helmstedt. Little else is known of his early years, but he obtained a degree of master of arts in Paris in 1351 and was made rector of the university in 1353. His writings consist mostly of books of questions on Aristotle's treatises and of some treatises of his own on logic and mathematical subjects.

His importance in the history of science is mainly as a transmitter and compiler of ideas drawn from the works of Buridan, William of Ockham, Burley, Oresme, and others in the mediaeval scientific tradition. The present work on Aristotle's *De caelo et mundo* was first published in 1481.

GW 797; H 577; BMC V, 569; Goff A-348; Pell 388; IGI 252; Klebs 30.3.

71   Etymologikon mega kata alphabeton (Graece).

Venice, Zacharias Kallierges for Nikolaos Blastos and Anna Notaras,
8 July 1499

Large folio (395 × 270 mm.). Greek type. 50 lines. 2 cols. [224] ff. (small ink stain on one leaf). 23 woodcut head-pieces, 10- and 5-line woodcut initials, Blastos's large woodcut device below colophon and printer's smaller device below register, all printed in red, as are all headings, brackets, capital letters to each entry, and signature of first quire. Sixteenth-century dark brown calf, possibly Swiss, roll-stamped in blind with roses, sprays of foliage, wyverns and griffins (rebacked and corners restored, ties gone). From the libraries of Agostino Giustiniani, with his ms. exlibris on first text leaf; and of Estelle Doheny, with her leather bookplate.

First edition of this mediaeval Greek dictionary, edited by Marcus Musurus, and the first production from the first press of Zacharias Kallierges. The editor, printer, and publisher were all natives of Crete. According to Proctor, it took five years for Kallierges to produce the Greek type used here. It turned out to have been well worth the labor for it is extremely beautiful, being both dignified and delicate. Also of great beauty are the elaborate head-pieces and initials, filled with arabesques, and the unusually delicate device of Blastos. The work begins with a poem and preface by Musurus, the latter describing the long gestatory period and production of the type.

Agostino Giustiniani, a Dominican who became bishop of Nebbio, was born at Genoa in 1470 and perished at sea in 1536. An expert in Oriental languages, he edited the 1516 Genoa polyglot Psalter, which he published at his own expense.

A fine copy of one of the most beautiful Greek books of the time.

GW 9426; HC 6691; BMC V, 580; Goff E-112; Pell 4629; Pol 1423; IGI 3720; IDL 1729; Sander 7710; Essling 1184; Doheny Cat. I, 10; Proctor, *Printing of Greek in 15th c.,* pp. 117–125.

ΑΡΧΗ ΤΟΥ ΖΗΤΑ ΣΤΟΙΧΕΙΟΥ :~

Ητα ςτοιχεῖον, ἀπὸ τοῦ ζέω τοῦ βορέου. σύμμυκται ἀπὸ λῷος.

Ζαβάλλω, τὸ ζαπατῶ.

Ζαλαίνω, τὸ μωραίνω.

Ζαβουλών. πρὰ ρ ζα ἐπιτατικὸν μόριον, καὶ ρ βουλή, γίνεται ζαβουλών. ὁ πάνυ βουλευτικώτατος.

Ζαγρεύς, ὁ Διόνυσος, πρὰ τοῖς ποιηταῖς. δοκεῖ γὰρ ζῶ ζῆμ ἡρῆσθαι τὸν τῷ σεφόνη. ἐξῆς ὁ ὅμοιος ὁ Διόνυσος. καλλίμαχος. Υ ὃ διόνυσον Ζαγρέα γεναμένη. πρὰ τὸ ζα, ἤγοντα ναγένεω. τινὲς ἄλλον φασὶν εἶναι τῷ πλούτωνι.

Ζάγκλον, τὸ δρέπανον. ὡς φησι καλλίμαχος. Κερκυραίη γὴν ζάγκλον ὑπὸ χθονί. πρὰ τὸ ζα ἐπιτατικὸν μόριον ἢ τὸ ἄγκυλον, ζάγκυλον. κὴ ἐκ συγκοπῆς, ζάγκλον. ρ

Ζαης, ὁ σφοδρὸς ἄνεμος. ὅμηρος. Ζαῆϊ ἀνέμῳ. ὤρσε δῶ ζαῆ ἄνεμον. τὸν σφοδρῶς πνέοντα. ἀπὸ τοῦ ζα καὶ τοῦ ἄω τὸ πνέω, γίνεται ζαης. καὶ συστολῇ αἰολικῇ, ζαης. κ ὡς πρὰ τὸ πέτω γίνεται πέτην. οὕτω καὶ πρὰ τὸ ἄω, ἄην κ ζάην ρ τὸ ζα. τὸ γὰρ τέλτον ζα ἤγουν ὡς πέτην, ἀλλα κατ ἐκλιτιν γέγονε.

Ζάθεος, ἅγιος. εὐδαίμων. μεγαλόθιμος. εὐώδης. κὸ πάν ρυθμος καὶ θειότατος. πρὰ τὸ θεὸς ἢ ρ ἐπιτατικὸν, ἄθεος. καὶ αἰολικῶς γέγονεν. οἱ δὲ αἰολεῖς τὸ διὰ ζα φασι. κὴ ρ διὰ πλεύρου, ζάπλουρον. κὴ πρὰ ρ ζα ἐπιτατικὸν κὴ τὸ θέω, ἢ ὁ ἀξιοθέατος. ὡς καὶ ἡ ζάθεος, ὁ ἄξιαν τῆς θέας μετέχων. ὁ θαυμαστός. τὸ δὲ ζα, ρ μεγα κὸ ἰσχυρὸν καὶ ζαθέην. ἐκ τοῦ ζα κὴ τοῦ θεος, γίνεται ζαθέα. ζ πολύ θʹ. Εἰ Ιωνικῶ τὸ πᾶν τῷ αζ εἰσιν, ζαθέη. Κίλλαντε ζαθέην, τὴν ἁγίαν ἢ θείαν καὶ θαυμαστήν.

Ζαθερές, ρ μεσημβρινὸν καῦμα.

Ζάπυρος, ὁ ἄγαν ὀργίλος. ὁ μεγαλόπυρος. κὸ πρὸς τὸ ὀργῆ. ἡ δὲ πρόθεσίς ἐστιν ὅτε κ ἐπιτατικόν. κ ρ ἐπομένη ὑπὸ αἰολέων, γίνεται ζα. ὡς πρὰ ρ διαφλεγης, ζαφλεγης. καὶ ρ ἁπλῶς τὸ διὰ εἴτε πρόθεσιν σημαίνει εἴτε μόνας συλλαβάς, ρἔπεται ἀς ζα. κὴ τὸ τὴν καρδίαν, κὴ ρ δ ναπενεῖς, ζαμενής.

Ζάκορος, νεωκόρος. ἤγουν ἡ διακονοῦσα πρ ἱερῶ.

μῦ ἀνδρος. Ζάπυρος ἡ κοσμοῦσα τῇ ηγαῖῷ τέκνον. κὴ δὺ πρέπης. Λευκαδία, βλάπτεις τὸ πῦρ ἡ ζάπυρος οὕτω σὶ καλῶς. κ οἱ ἱερεὺς ὀργᾶν ἡ κοσμῶν τὸ σαρῶν. καρδὴ γὰρ τὸ σαίρῃ πρὰ τῖ ποιεῖς. τὸ δὲ ζα οὐκ ἔτι ἐν ταῦτα ἐπιτατικόν, ἀλλ' ἀπὸ τῆς διὰ προθέσεως. ἡ ἢ διάπυρος. καὶ ἀττικῶς, καὶ αἰολικῶς.

Ζάλη, τὴν σύμβροντον πνοήν, ἢ τὴν μεγάλην ἄελα ἢ τὴν ταραχὴν τῆς θαλάσσης, ἢ τοῦ ἀέρος. ἀπὸ τοῦ σφόδρα ἀλίζεσθαι. πρὰ ρ ζα καὶ τὴν ἄελαν. πλάτων. Εἴτε ζάλη πνεύματος ὑπὸ ἀέρος φαινομένη καὶ ἀλειφθῆναι συστροφῆ γὰρ καὶ συρμὸν βούλεται δηλοῦν. τι πρὸς ἄνεμος λάβρος. πνεῦμα θορυβῶδες. Κλήμης δύναται ζάλην τίς εἶναι, μεγάλου στροφή ἀνέμου. τὶ πρὸς ζάλην τὴν χέλαζαν. ἢ πρὰ ρ ζ ἐπὶ τὴν ἄελα, ἤγουν ἐπι κορυφοῦσθαι ὑπὸ τῶν ἀνέμων. ἡ κέουσα κυρίως γὰρ ἐπὶ τῆς θαλάσσης. πρὰ ρ ζ ἐπι τὴν ἄελα.

Ζαμενής, εὔψυχος. μεγα μένος ἔχων, ρυ τιὲ ψυχὴν προθυμίαν. ἢ ὁ ἄγαν ὀργίλος. πρὰ ρ μένος ὁ σημαίνει τὴν ὀργὴν καὶ τὸν θυμόν.

Ζάμολξις, πυθαγόρα δουλεύσας ἃς ἡ ρόθορος τετάρτη σκύθης. ὃς ἐπανελθὼν, ἐδίδασκε πὲ τοῦ ἀθά παρὸν εἶναι τὴν ψυχήν. μιμησάμενος δὲ πρὰ γε τους, τὸ χρόνον τιμᾶσθαι καὶ καλεῖσθαι ζάμολξον. φανῖνος δὲ ἐν τοῖς βαρβαρικοῖς νόμοις φησὶν, ὅτι δὴ κτηνὸς τε τε πῶς. πλεῖται κατέλιπε τε τοὺς πρὶς σφραγμι. καὶ ἐ λει ἐν οὗ τὰν ἄλλος ἀπὸ θανὼν οὐδοὶ μετὰ ρύρυ, ἐξουσι πάντα τὰ ζαθὰ ἄμα δὲ τῷ ταλέγω, ανο δλι μ οἴκημα κατὰ ζαιον. ἐ ἐν τα ἀφανισθεὶς, ἀφνίδιον ἐκ δρακῶν ἐν τούτῳ τῷ δη τὰρ. οἱ δὲ γέται ἐπὸθοῦ ἄλλον. τε τάρτα δὲ ἔτει πάλιν φαίνεται. ὃ οἱ θρᾶκες ἄλλ τῳ τα βιστεύσας. λέγουσι δʹ πι πρέσας ὁ ζάμολξις ἐδούλευσε τῷ πυθαγόρα καὶ ἐλευθερωθείς, τὰ ζ ἐσσοιπι. ἀνὰ πολὺ πρότε ρον πμι δοκοῦσο ζά μολξις πυθαγόρας γενέσθαι. ἀθανατίζουσι δὲ καὶ τε ρίζοι καὶ πρόβυλοι. καὶ τοῖς ἀποθανόντας ὡς ζάμολξιν φασι ποι χεσθαι, ἥξει δὲ αὖθις. καὶ τούτα ἀεὶ πμι ζου σι ἀληθεύσιν. θύουσι δὲ ζ ευοχούν τα ὡς αὐθις ἕξον.

Ζάραξ. λυπισφῶν. Ὀφέλτα ρος τοῦ ἀποθανόντος. καὶ μήχρυ ε ἐχοιρὰ δὴ ζάραξ. ζάραξ καὶ ὁ Ὀφέλτα, ὃς ἐν εὐβοίας πλεῖ γέγονε Ιαμαχλάσια τῶν ἑλλήνων. ζάραξ δὲ ὠνόμασαι ἀπὸ ζάρακος τοῦ περαίου τοῦ καρύστου.

72   [PROCOPIUS OF CAESAREA.] – BRUNUS ARETINUS, LEONARDUS, *trans. & ed.* De bello Italico adversus Gothos.

> Foligno, Johann Numeister & Emilio de Orfini (i.e. Orsini), 1470

Small folio (276 × 212 mm.). Roman type. 29 lines. [73] ff. (of 74, lacking initial blank, but last blank present; washed, with faint traces of early marginalia; first leaf rehinged and with very slight browning). Blank spaces for capitals. 18th century vellum, morocco labels on spine. From the libraries of Girolamo d'Adda; and of Eric Sexton, with their bookplates.

First book printed at Foligno and the first edition of this work on the war against the Ostrogoths in Italy and Sicily in the sixth century. According to Claudin, Numeister (or Neumeister, as he called himself later in France) was Gutenberg's assistant after the collapse of the partnership with Fust, but the sole evidence for this was an inscription (reported by Gotthelf Fischer in 1802) in a volume in the Carthusian Library at Mainz - a volume no longer extant. Numeister also printed the Foligno Dante in 1472.

The present copy has fine, large margins and though not quite as tall as the BMC copy, it is 12 mm. wider.

Girolamo d'Adda (1815-1881) was a noted Italian bibliophile and collector, and author of a work on the library of Leonardo da Vinci. At the end of the nineteenth century his entire library was purchased by Charles Fairfax Murray who issued the *Catalogo dei Libri proveniente dalla Biblioteca del Marchese Girolamo d'Adda* (1902). A copy of *De bello Italico* is listed both in this catalogue (no. 203) and in the Fairfax Murray sale catalogue of 1922, so it would seem that this famous name can also be added to the provenance.

GW 5600; HC 1558; BMC VI, 599; Goff B-1234; Pell 1112; IGI 2188; Claudin, "Les Peregrinations de J. Neumeister" in his *Origines de l'Imprimerie a Albi* (1880), pp. 45–46; Deschamps, p. 535–6.

ONE OF THE GREAT MONUMENTS OF ITALIAN RENAISSANCE WOODCUT ILLUSTRATION

73   JACOBUS PHILIPPUS FORESTI BERGOMENSIS. – ALBERTUS DE PLACENTIA AND AUGUSTINUS DE CASALI MAIORI, *eds.* De plurimis claris sceletisque Mulieribus.

> Ferrara, Laurentius de Rubeis, de Valentia, 29 April 1497

Folio (310 × 205 mm.). Gothic type. 45 lines. [4], CLXX (i.e. CLXXII) ff. (3 minor marginal repairs; few insignificant stains). Xylographic title; 2 full-page woodcuts (the author presenting his book to Beatrice of Aragon,

De
plurimis
claris selectis q̃
mulieribus. Opus
prope diuinū
nouissime
conge
stum

widow of Matthias Corvinus, and 8 scenes from the life of the Virgin), both enclosed in identical woodcut borders, a full woodcut border enclosing the beginning of the main body of text, the first two with some light yellow coloring in a few places; 172 woodcut portraits (including 116 repeats); large historiated woodcut initial M; numerous decorative 4-line initials, white on black; capitals touched in red, chapter headings underlined in red. 19th-century gold-ruled calf, back gilt, with leather labels. From the libraries of Jan Jacob, count Nahuys, with his circular stamp in lower margin of title; of Sir Thomas Brooke, with his bookplate (his son's sale, Sotheby, 25 May 1921, lot 89); of Carl J. Ulmann, with his leather bookplate (his sale, Parke-Bernet, 15 April 1952, lot 24); and of Estelle Doheny, with her leather bookplate.

Composed by Giacomo Filippo Foresti da Bergamo (1434-1520), the work recounts the lives of women famous in history and mythology, each accompanied by a woodcut portrait set in a landscape. At least seven of the cuts towards the end are not repeated, and show such lifelike detail that it is generally agreed that they were taken from contemporary portraits.

This is one of the great illustrated books of the Italian Renaissance, although no artist has been identified. The outline borders of putti with musical instruments, griffins, etc. are in the Venetian style, and all woodcut material appears here for the first time.

A fine copy with good margins and provenance.

HC 2813; BMC VI, 613; Goff J-204; Pell 2069; Pol 1497; IGI 5071; IDL 2608; Sander 915; Schäfer 186; Hind II, 510-12; Brooke Cat. I, 46; Doheny Cat. III, 17.

THE EDITIO PRINCEPS OF HOMER

74 HOMERUS. – CHALCONDYLAS, DEMETRIUS, *ed.* Opera (Graece).

> Florence, [Bartolommeo de Libri?] and Demetrius Damilas for the
> brothers Bernardus and Nerius Nerlius, 9 December 1488
> (but not before 13 January 1488–89, date of dedication)

Folio (335 & 320 × 210 mm.) 2 vols. Greek type. 39 lines. [439] ff. (of 440, lacking final blank, but including blank at f. 42; vol. II somewhat shorter than vol. I; two text pages O$_2$v and O$_7$ reversed in imposition, as in BMC copy; first few leaves foxed; a few worm-punctures at beginning of v. 2). Early 19th-century English russia, gold-ruled; gilt inner dentelles. From the library of Dr. Charles Burney (1757–1817), whose collection was sold after his death to the British Museum, and with their library stamps (sold as duplicate July 1931); and from the library of Estelle Doheny, with her leather bookplate.

The editio princeps of all Homer's works (except the Batrachomyomachia), edited by the great Greek scholar Demetrio Chalcondylas (b. Athens, 1423, d. Milan 1511). This is the most extensive piece of Greek printing undertaken up to that date, employing a recasting of the type used by Damilas for the Laskaris *Erotema*. In the dedication to Piero de' Medici, Bernardo Nerli acknowledges the support of his brother Neri, with financial assistance from Giovanni Acciaiuoli.

The misimposition in this copy is noted in a beautiful Greek hand (possibly that of Chalcondylas) inserting the first line of the correct text in each case. Both Proctor (*The Printing of Greek*) and Ridolfi (*La Stampa in Firenze nel secolo XV*, chapter 7) discuss the most likely Florentine printing shop which Damilas and the Nerlis might have used for this Homer.

A very handsome set of this magnificent example of the early printing of Greek, though the discrepancy in size between the two volumes may mean that they did not form a set before Burney owned them.

HCR 8772; BMC VI, 678; Goff H-300; Pol 1983; BNIC H-173; IGI 4795; IDL 2350; Doheny I, 10; Proctor, *op. cit.*, pp. 66–69.

RARE INCUNABULUM, NOT IN GOFF

75 AUGUSTINUS [DE NOVIS] PAPIENSIS. Scrutinium consiliorum quatriconsulti collegii.

Florence, Bartolommeo di Libri, 25 April 1500

Folio (320 × 233 mm.). Roman type. 48-49 lines commentary surrounding text of varying size. [144] ff. (small stab hole in first five quires occasionally affecting a letter of text; penultimate leaf with some stains; few scattered worm-punctures at end; lower outer corners of last few leaves a little frayed). Decorative woodcut initials, white on black. 19th-century vellum. Some contemporary marginalia. From the Royal University Library at Padua, with three small library stamps; and from the library of Henri Soret, with his label.

First edition, first issue. The work is a commentary by Augustinus (d. 1520) on numerous *consilia* on behalf of the monastic orders delivered by *collegia* of lawyers against the Augustinian Canons. The author was himself an Augustinian Canon and Rector General of his order in 1497, and he develops a spirited defence of it in the present book.

At the end is a short history of the Order, followed by brief accounts of other orders. The briefest of all is the description that of the Templars, which simply states that it was founded in 1124 and exterminated by Philip of France.

A well-printed work in two sizes of roman type, and the last dated incunabulum from the press of Bartolommeo di Libri. No copy recorded in Goff.

GW 3062; HC 2115; BMC VI, 654; IGI 1071; not in Pell, Pol, or IDL.

76 MICHAEL SCOTUS. Expositio super auctorum sp[h]erae.

Bologna, Justinianus de Ruberia, 16 September 1495

Small 4to (197 × 151 mm.). Gothic type. 38 lines. [40] ff. Large woodcut printer's device at end and one woodcut initial, both with contemporary hand coloring. Modern limp vellum. From the library of Harrison D. Horblit.

The first and only fifteenth-century edition of this commentary on the sphere of Sacrobosco, composed by Michael in the thirteenth century at the request of the Emperor Frederic II.

One of the back fly-leaves contains extensive astronomical notes in a late humanist hand.

HC 14555; BMC VI, 849; Goff M-550; IGI 6416; Klebs 900.1.

77 BIBLE. LATIN. [With additions by Biagio Romero and Thomas Taqui.]

Naples, Mathias Moravus [and Biagio Romero], 1476

Small folio (310 × 223 mm.). 2 vols. Gothic type. 52 lines and headline. 2 cols. (Interpretationes: 54 lines, 3 cols). [238] and [216] ff. = [454] ff. (first two leaves soiled, blank recto of f. 1 backed, 3 tears repaired, corner and portion of inner margin of last leaf renewed, a number of leaves rein-forced at inner margin, insignificant worming to first and last leaves not affecting text, a few headlines very slightly shaved). Initials and paragraph marks supplied in red. Eighteenth-century brown calf (rebacked, hinges weak), gilt panel design and inside dentelles, spine gilt. From the libraries of Michael Mangell (an Anglican, 1666); and of James Darcy (a Fran-ciscan, 1678), with their ms. exlibris under the prefatory letters; of Charles Spencer, third earl of Sunderland, with his ink shelf-marks on front fly-leaves (his sale, Puttick & Simpson, 6 Dec. 1881, no. 1340, bought by Quaritch, with a bookplate noting this purchase); of William Makellar (his sale, Sotheby, 7 Nov. 1898, no. 481); and of the General Theological Seminary with its bookplates and unobtrusive embossed stamps.

The first Bible printed at Naples and the first to contain printed signature marks. Its text is based on the first Venetian Bible of 1475 and is preceded by an epistle of the printer's assistant, the Cistercian Biagio Romero, to Thomas Taqui, agent of Louis XI, and the latter's answer. Added are 34 leaves of *Interpretationes hebraicorum nominum.*

A typographically important edition of the Bible, with a distinguished prov-enance. As far as we could determine, only one other complete copy has been on the market in this century.

GW 4220; HC 3059; BMC VI 862; Goff B-545; Pell 2289; IGI 1645; Fava/Bresciano 110; Copinger, *Inc. Bibl.* 31.

❧ SWITZERLAND ❧

WITH THE RUBRICATOR'S ACQUISITION NOTE, 1475

78   BIBLE. LATIN. [With additions by Menardus Monachus].

[Basel, Bernhard Richel], 1475

(*Bound with:*) Interpretationes Hebraicorum nominum.

Basel, Bernhard Richel, 8 September 1477

Folio (I and III: 344 × 256 mm., II: 344 × 275 mm.). Gothic type. 48 lines and headline. 2 cols. [461]; [40] ff., bound in 3 vols. of 227, 234, and 40 ff. (initial blank silked; second leaf soiled, with small hole between columns, lower margin reinforced; first four quires and a few other leaves lightly dampstained; light worming to beginnings of vols. 1 and 2, end of v. 2, and to v. 3). Numerous woodcut initials ranging from c. 55 mm. square to c. 24 mm. square, many of them rubricated, some hand-colored, one with scroll-work extending into margin; incipits and some headlines printed in red; capitals touched in red, foliation in v. 2 supplied in red, rubricator's date "Anno 1475" at end. Modern red levant morocco (III: matching three-quarter morocco), spines gold-lettered, g.e., by Semet & Plumelle; in morocco-tipped slipcases. From the libraries of the rubricator Heinrich Höfer; with his acquisition note on f. 359v; of the monastery of Sts. Ulrich and Afra (near Augsburg), with its ms. exlibris in v. 2; and of the General Theological Seminary (New York), with its bookplates and unobtrusive embossed stamps.

A highly interesting association copy, its first owner being also its rubricator, Heinrich Höfer. On f. 359v (= II, 132v) he noted in rubricator's ink and in a script imitating Richel's type "Anno Mᵒ cccc Lccquinto ultima mensis Octobris Iste liber per me h[enri]cum höfer empt[us] est." This not only reveals the name of the usually anonymous rubricator, but is also one of the rare instances of a 15th-century acquisition note dating from the year of publication.

Added to the Bible text are the canons of Eusebius, the Harmony of the Four Evangelists, and an account of the contents written by Menardus Monachus, representing, after Richel's undated edition of c. 1474, the earliest attempt to add scholarship to the Bible text. The added thin volume listing all Hebrew names in the Bible was first published as part of Richel's 1477 edition. Added at front of v. 2 is a register leaf, apparently in Höfer's hand. This is the variant issue (cf. GW), with an additional blank leaf at the beginning.

Bible: GW 4215 and note: HC 3053; BMC III, 736; Goff B-540; Pell 2277; IGI 1640; IDL 815; Copinger, *Inc. Bibl.* 19; Berkowitz, *In remembrance,* 94.

Interpretationes: GW 4228; HC 3064; BMC III, 737; Goff B-553; Pell 2293; Pol 646; IGI 1652; IDL 822; Copinger, *Inc. Bibl.* 33.

79   BIBLE. LATIN. [With additions by Menardus Monachus.]

Basel, Bernhard Richel, 8 September 1477

Folio (402 × 284 mm.). Gothic type. 50 lines ("Interpretationes": 61 lines). 2 cols. [525] ff. (of 526, lacking blank leaf preceding "Interpretationes"; initial blank leaf present), bound in 2 vols of 276 and 249 leaves, with the "Interpretationes" (39 ff.) bound in at the beginning (light dampstaining mostly restricted to margins; marginal worming to early leaves of v. 1; slight wear to lower corners of last few leaves; two marginal tears repaired). First text-page with 10-line initial illuminated in green on red and gold background, with colored foliate sprays and penwork decoration extending into the margins. Numerous decorative woodcut initials in seven different styles and sizes, the largest c. 55 mm. square, in v. 2; capital spaces, often with guide letters, in v. 1. Printer's device and colophon, headlines, some incipits and explicits, and Hebrew alphabet in "Lamentations" printed in red. Many initials in v. 1 supplied in red, some woodcut initials touched in red; partially rubricated, often first leaf of each quire only. Modern dark brown calf, blind-ruled, spine gold-lettered, g.e. From the libraries of William Makellar (his sale, Sotheby's, 7 Nov. 1898, no. 482); and of the General Theological Seminary (New York), with its unobtrusive embossed stamps.

A beautifully produced Bible, advantageously using three different fonts of gothic type and seven sets of decorative woodcut initials. This is the third Bible printed by Richel and the first to contain the impressive 78-page index to Hebrew names ("Interpretationes hebraicorum nominum").

"Of very rare occurence" (Copinger)

GW 4228; HC 3064; BMC III, 737-8; Goff B-553; Pell 2293; Pol 646; IGI 1652; Copinger, *Inc. Bibl.* 33.

80   PETRUS LOMBARDUS. Sententiarum libri IV.

[Basel, Bernhard Richel, c. 1482]

Folio (298 × 203 mm.). Gothic type. 49 lines. 2 cols. [280] ff., including blank ff. 104 and 144 (first leaf lightly soiled, occasional thumbing). Large initials supplied in red, headings underlined and capitals touched in red. Old vellum. A few early marginalia. Ms. exlibris of the library of the Piarist School at Schlackenwerth, Bohemia (today Ostrov, Czechoslovakia), stating it was formerly owned by Princess Piccolomini.

A handsome edition of the famous *Sententiae* of Petrus Lombardus, written between 1148 and 1150. This theological handbook is primarily a collection of opinions of the fathers of the Church, arranged on the basis of the aphorisms of

Augustine, the author's favorite authority. It is divided into four books, the first treating of God, the second of the Creation and Sin, the third of the Incarnation and the Virtues, and the fourth of the Sacraments and the Four Last Things. This work became the standard textbook of Catholic theology during the Middle Ages, and was the subject of numerous commentaries, finally being superseded by the Summa of St. Thomas Aquinas. The "Master of the Sentences", as he became known, was born near Novara in Lombardy, studied at Bologna and Rheims, and taught at the Cathedral School in Paris, to which city he was appointed Bishop shortly before his death in 1160.

This work was formerly attributed by Proctor to the press of Nicolaus Kesler in Basel, but subsequently assigned to that of Richel.

A fine, well-preserved copy of one of the great manuals of the Middle Ages, perhaps once owned by the wife or daughter of the famous general Ottavio Piccolomini, who was made prince.

H C 10185; BMC III, 739; Goff P-482; Pol 3112; IGI 7636; IDL 3660.

BY THE "FATHER" OF BIBLIOGRAPHY

81 TRITHEMIUS, JOHANNES. Liber de Scriptoribus Ecclesiasticis.
Basel, Johann Amerbach, [after 28 August] 1494

Folio (292 × 205 mm.). Roman type. 51 lines. [6], 140, [1] ff. (final blank not present). 16th-century limp vellum with ties (one lacking); ms. title on spine. Unidentified shelf locations on title.

First edition of the first modern systematic bibliography, the author's most important work and the one which earned him the title of "Father of Bibliography". It lists in chronological order 982 authors, with all their known works, amounting to about seven thousand titles. An alphabetical list arranged by first names of authors serves as an index at the beginning of the book, and contrary to the implication of the title includes numerous lay authors, the humanists and scholars who were Trithemius' contemporaries.

It is interesting to note that his Preface contains those same elements so often present in most bibliographies since 1494, i.e., apologies for incompleteness, awareness of imperfections, and the enormous amount of work achieved only "magnis sudoribus & expensis".

Trithemius, Abbot of the Benedictine abbey of Sponheim and then of St. James in Würzburg, was an experienced librarian and cataloguer and had a passion for system and order as well as for books, the two necessary requirements for a bibliographer.

This is a fine, tall, crisp copy in a sound and unexceptionable early binding.

HC 15619; BMC III, 755; Goff T-452; Pol 3820; Klebs 990.1; Folter-Breslauer 7; Besterman, *Beginnings*, p. 6ff.

82 EYB, ALBERT VON. Margarita poetica.

Basel, Johann Amerbach, 1495

Small folio (273 × 200 mm.). Roman type. 55 lines. [244] ff. (2 tiny worm‑punctures in blank fore margin of last few quires, and 1 in lower margin of first 3 ff.). 1 maiblumen initial at beginning of first part supplied in red and dark brown ink, other initials of varying size supplied in red, together with paragraph marks and underlining of headlines and chapter headings; capi‑tals touched in red throughout. 18th‑century brown calf, back elaborately gilt (repairs to joints; some slight scuffing and staining on sides). According to the contemporary inscription on the original flyleaf, this copy was presented by the printer to the Charterhouse in Basel, and bears the exlibris of that institution on the title to the Subject Index; engraved bookplate of Jacques Teutsch.

A very fine edition of this work of early German Humanism, entitled *Margarita poetica* in honor of the author's mother, Margarete von Wolmershausen. It com‑prises instruction in the writing of elegant letters and in eloquence generally, and was a popular manual for many years. The text was of selected passages from classical and contemporary poets and authors – Cicero, Virgil, Petrarch, etc. The 20 leaves of the *Annotatio*, the Subject Index, are bound in before the text, and constitute the most voluminous index up to this date.

The typography in this volume represents some of Amerbach's most elegant work.

BMC states that Amerbach gave two copies of this book to the Charterhouse in Basel in 1496, instead of the customary one, so this is undoubtedly the second copy (BMC III, xxxv, 742 and 756).

GW 9537; HC 6825; BMC III, 756; Goff E‑178; Pol 1451; Pell 4707; IGI 3777; IDL 1767.

83 PHILELPHUS, FRANCISCUS. Orationes cum quibusdam aliis eiusdam operibus.

[Basel, Johann Amerbach, c. 1495]

4to (215 × 153 mm.). Roman type. 40 lines. [182] ff. (one leaf near begin‑ning lightly browned). Large initial "S" in red and blue with internal tendril decoration on opening page of text; numerous other initials supplied in red or blue. Old marbled boards. Ms. exlibris of Dominican monastery of Rott‑weil on title; Ms. exlibris of John Valentin Deyger of Strassburg on front endpaper, noting that he bought the book for 41 denarii, 2 March, '38 (1538); below this another exlibris dated '41 and the price of 4 batzen.

pauperior certe futur⁹ nõ fũ: at fi tibi quæ petieras fecero: iniuftior.

Cyrus Yrus iunior cũ Lacedæmonios ut fecũ focietatẽ facerẽt horta
rẽt: dicebat cor fibi lõge graui⁹ effe q̃ fratri quodq̃ & plus me
ri q̃ ille biberet: & meli⁹ ferret: & ut ille uix in uenatiõib⁹ equis infi
fteret: at difficiliorib⁹ in reb⁹ ne in folio quidẽ. Hortabaf aũt uiros
ad fe mitterẽt: monẽs ac pollicẽs peditib⁹ equos fe datuꝝ: equitib⁹
uero bigas: uicos aũt quib⁹ prædia effent: at eos q uicos poffiderẽt
factuꝝ fe urbiũ dños: argẽti ꝑo & auri nõ numeꝝ fed põd⁹ ijs fore.

Artaxerxes Rtaxerxes hui⁹ frater cognomẽto memor: nõ adeũtibus mõ
fed obfequentẽ benignũq̃ præftabat: ueꝝ etiã legitimæ uxori
iufferat: regij curr⁹ aulea undiq̃ tolleret: q̃ indigẽtib⁹ in itinere adi
tus pateret. Paupere aũt hoie malũ ingẽtis magnitudinis ei offerẽ
te iucũde fufcepit: ꝑ fole inquiẽs hic is mihi uidef: quẽ urbẽ q̃ ex'p'
ua magnã reddere poffe exiftimẽ. Cum uero aliqñ fugiẽs cõmeatu
impedimẽtifq̃ direptis: ficcis ficis uefceref ac pane ordeacco: cuiuf
modi inquit uoluptatis rudis eram.

Paryfatis Aryfatis filia Cyri & Artaxerxis mater: iubebat: qui rex ap
Cyrus rex parate quippiã & imperio fe dicturus effet: ucrbif grauiffimis
Artaxerxes atq̃ ornatiffimis uteretur.
rex

Orontes Rontes regis Artaxerxis gener: cũ ob irã in ignominiã excidif
fet: cõtemptuiq̃ effet: inqt: quẽadmodũ cõputatoꝝ digiti nũc
decies millenarios numeros: nũc unarios queũt ponere: eodem q̃
modo regũ amicos poffe qñq̃ totũ qñq̃ minimũ.

Memnon Emnon qui cõtra Alexandrũ pro rege Dario bellum gereret:
Darius quendã qui fub fe merens multa de Alexandro maledice pe
Alexãder rex tulanterq̃ loqueref: ubi lancea percuffiffet: Ego te inquit alo ut pu
gnes: nõ ut maledicas Alexandro.

Reges ægyp Egyptioꝝ reges ꝑ fui ipfoq̃ lege adiurabãt iudices: ne q̃d per
tiorum iniuriã aliqñ iudicarẽt: fi reges id etiã ipfi imperaffent.

Poltys rex Oltys rex Thracũ cũ in Troiano bello: & a Troianis eũ & ab
Helena Acheis legati fimul adijffent: iuffit ut Helenã redderẽt duafq̃
a fe pulchras muleres Alexander acciperet.

Teres Eres Sitalci pater dicere cõfueuit cũ ociofus effet neq̃ rei mili
Sitalcus tari opurã daret: nihilo fe fua fentẽtia agafonib⁹ præftare.
Cotys

Otys pardã largiẽti: leonẽ ipfe cõtra largituf eft. Cũq̃ natura
excãdefceret & in eos q in minifterijf deliquiffent aïaduerteret
graui⁹: ubi ab pegrino uafa fictilia deportata forẽt: & cũ & fragilia
& tenuia: tũ etiã apte atq̃ magnifice laborata: cælata: tornataq̃ po
litiffime: peregrino qdẽ illi dedit dona: at uafa cõfregit oïa: ne ꝑ irã
ut ait: amarius illos plecteret qui ea cõfregiffent.

A fine copy with most beautifully written initials. Francesco Filelfo (1398–1481), Italian humanist, conducted his early studies in grammar, rhetoric and Latin at Padua where he acquired so great a reputation that he was invited to teach at Venice. Residence at Constantinople as secretary to the Venetian consul/general enabled him to learn Greek. Returning to Italy, he settled in Florence, but a violent animosity developed between him and Cosimo de' Medici. He moved to Siena and then to Milan. Here he celebrated his princely patrons in panegyrics and abused their enemies with invective. Finally, as an old man of seventy/seven he went to Rome, but managed to upset Sixtus IV and had to leave the city. He died in Florence at the age of 83, where he had been invited to profess Greek.

Johann Valentin Deyger whose ms. exlibris appears in this volume, played an active role in the Reformation and at the time of the Augsburg Interim of 1548 fled his parish of Strassburg for Basel. An Album Amicorum of his appeared in the Landau sale of October 1948.

HC 12918; BMC III, 757; Goff P/612; Pol 3138; IGI 3909; IDL 3688; Klebs 403.5.

IN THE ORIGINAL BINDING

84 JOHANNES NIVICELLENSIS [ABBOT OF NIVELLE]. Concordan/tie Biblie [et] Canonum.

[Basel, Nicolaus Kesler, c. 1488]

Folio. (292 × 208 mm.). Gothic type. 54 lines. 2 cols. 1 f., [48] ff., 1 blank leaf (some worm/punctures in the first few leaves). Some contemporary marginalia.
(*Bound with:*) WIMPINA [OR KOCH], CONRAD. Epithoma: mire breviter, sed distincte satis amplectens, varia, et . . . doctorum problemata, opinationes, et Argume[n]ta, eoru[m], qui circa Sente[n]tiaru[m] libru [m].

Frankfurt an der Oder, Nicolaus Lamperter & Balthasar Murrer, 1 October 1508

Gothic type. 63 lines. 2 cols. [100] ff. (marginal tear in third leaf repaired). Capitals touched and headings underlined in red.
(*And with:*) THOMAS AQUINAS [SAINT]. Quodlibeta. Varie ques/tiones de quodlibet disputate ac edite a . . . Thoma Aquinate.

[Cologne, Heinrich Quentel], 1509

Gothic type. 57 lines. 2 cols. LXVI [i.e. 67], [3] ff. Large woodcut initial of the writing Saint on title, other large decorative woodcut initials filled with flowers or jesters; numerous four/ and two/line lombardic initials. Con/

temporary blind-tooled pigskin and bevelled oak boards, remains of clasps and catches (upper joint repaired). Some contemporary marginalia. From the libraries of Stanislaus Georg of Prufening, with his 16th-century ms. exlibris on title; of Charles D. March, with his ms. exlibris dated 9 May 1835; and of Patrick Brady, with a stamp noting his bequest to St. Joseph's Seminary, Dunwoodie NY, dated 1894.

A beautifully preserved collection of works forming a typical theology text-book at a German university in the period when Luther was at school, in the original binding.

Ad I: A concordance of the Bible written by the abbot of the Dominican monastery at Nivelles near Brussels, and first published in 1472.

Ad II: Excerpts from the opinions of various theologians on subjects treated in Petrus Lombardus' *Sentences*. The compiler was a renowned German theo-logian who taught at Leipzig. In 1506 he became the first rector and professor of theology at the newly founded Academy in Frankfurt-an-der-Oder, where this book was published. One of the rare early imprints from that city.

Ad III: Discussions on various subjects by the great saint, presented here in a beautifully printed and designed edition.

I: H 9412; BMC III, 773; Goff J-381.

II: BM, STC German p. 474; not in Adams.

III: Adams A-1414; not in BM.

No copy of the second and only 1 copy of the third in NUC.

85   GUILLERMUS PARISIENSIS. Postilla super epistolas et eva[n]gelia de te[m]pore et sanctis et pro defunctis.

Basel, Nicolas Kessler, 1 October 1492

8vo (214 × 155 mm.), 2 parts in 1. Gothic type. 49 lines, 2 cols. [162] ff. including 2 blanks, last leaf and f. 102 (few light stains, quires d–f with small wormhole in blank upper inner margins; tear repaired in lower margin of f. 8; ff. 73 and 80 strengthened in inner margins). Large Crucifixion woodcut (121 × 88 mm.) on title and 53 smaller text woodcuts (c. 68 × 50 mm.), including a few repeats. Initials and paragraph marks supplied in red, capitals touched in red. Original blind-stamped leather over wooden boards, with old ms. endleaves (repairs to back, and back endleaf either replaced or a pastedown removed); old brass clasp added.

A richly illustrated Basel imprint of this very popular work of which there were more than a hundred editions in the fifteenth century. Guillermus was a Dominican and professor of theology at Paris. He wrote his compilation in 1437 for the clergy and those who wished to understand the excerpts from the Epistles and Evangelists (commonly called Lessons) which are read at services through-out the church year.

The woodcuts are a little crude in design, but very lively and expressive and show, according to Schreiber, the influence of the Strassburg *Plenarium* of 1482. They appeared in the Basel edition of 1491, with one or two minor differences in the large woodcut.

A fine, complete, uncolored copy.

H 8279; BMC III, 770; Goff G-692; IGI 4629; Schreiber 4147; Schramm XXI, 19 pl. 725-767; Goff, "The Postilla of Guillermus P." in *Gutenberg-Jahrbuch* (1959) pp. 73-78, no. 75; Weisbach, p. 39, no. 17.

❦ FRANCE ❦

NO OTHER COPY RECORDED IN AMERICA: FROM THE FAIRFAX MURRAY
COLLECTION

86   Eruditorium penitentiale.

                       [Paris, Antoine Caillaut, c. 1487–1490]

Small 8vo (176 × 121 mm.). Gothic type. 25–26 lines. [76] ff. 17 large
woodcuts with double black-line borders. Light brown morocco, panelled
in blind and gilt, fleurons in the angles, back gilt, g.e., by Bedford. Unidentified armorial bookplate, most likely English 19th century; catalogue label
of Charles Fairfax Murray; bookplate of Nikolas P. Kampton.

The rare first edition of this beautiful little book which displays the remarkable
quality of woodcut illustration done in France at this time. There are two undated
editions of which this appears to be the earlier. It has the double frame present
around the woodcut on f. a8 and the text agrees completely with Pellechet's
identification of the first as opposed to the later edition. However, the present copy
has the full set of seventeen different cuts, whereas Schäfer (and Kraus *Cat. 93*)
both state that in the first edition the Accidia cut is repeated where the Luxuria
cut ought to be. Since everything else about this copy is consonant with its being
the first, it would seem likely that there are variants. Also, since the Fairfax Murray Cat. states that the Luxuria block, along with three others, had already been
used in Caillaut's *Le livre de bonnes meurs*, dated 1487 in its colophon, and since
the *Eruditorium* is now assigned to the period 1487–1490, then it would seem most
likely that the cut was used initially and then misplaced or damaged by the time
the second edition was printed, and the repeat of the Accidia consequently
substituted.

The work begins with a title-leaf, followed by a woodcut of a Confessor and
a Penitent on the second leaf. This and the other sixteen cuts are all in outline
with slight hatching, a distinctive feature being the thick double black line border
to each; several cuts have xylographic inscriptions. The most striking blocks are
those representing the Seven Cardinal Sins, in which men are shown in attitudes
or actions characteristic of those vices and riding upon animals which were also
supposed to have similar propensities.

A superb example of the French illustrated incunabulum and one of great
rarity. Other than this copy, it is represented in North America only by the one-
line title-page in LC. GW locates only 9 copies, some incomplete. BMC has
only second edition, as has PML.

    GW 9390; H 13152 (either edition); Goff E-107; Pell 4622; Pol 1420; Fairfax Murray
155 (this copy); Schäfer 126; Claudin I, pp. 306–8 and 321–2; Kraus *Cat. 93*, no. 54.

Gula

Gula est causa solutionis corporis illecebrosi=
tas ciborul et auidus appetitus; Vel gula est ratio
nis sepulchrul aceruus stercoril origo luxurie ma=
ter nausee.

i.iii.

87 BOUTILLIER, JEAN. La somme rurale.

Paris, [Antoine Vérard? or Pierre Levet?], 1488

Small folio (264 × 190 mm.). Gothic type. 38 lines. 2 cols. [12], 208; 86, [5] = 311 ff. (of 312, last blank not present). Initials and paragraph marks supplied in red. 17th-century mottled sheep (upper joint starting), gilt-tooled compartments on back. From the library of the Flaghac family (see below); and of Julian Dejon, with his ms. exlibris "ex dono domini grangier" on first page.

A very rare edition of this important law book. This is the third edition, the first having been printed by Colard Mansion in Bruges, in 1479. Only one other copy is recorded in America.

The *Somme Rurale* is a popular codification of civil and criminal law, compiled for the use of country gentlemen, many of whom served as justices of the peace in their localities. Matters such as hunting and fishing rights, stray animals, sales of land, etc., are noted, as well as more general provisions regarding contracts, inheritances, crimes, etc. The work was highly regarded and printed many times during the next century and a half. Boutillier (d. 1395 or 1396) was a jurist of Tournai and his book is particularly relevant to that and surrounding areas such as Artois, Hainaut, and Flanders, though it was used for the whole of northern France and northwest Belgium. According to a note at the beginning of the text, the work was copied and revised in 1395-1450 by a law clerk under the Bailiff of Amiens. Boutillier's testament at the end is dated 1402 (but some mss. bear the date of 1395).

The work is in two parts. On the verso of f. 12 is the 16th-century ms. motto in red "Cest asses Flaghac" (repeated and deleted on f.L6v), and there are some brief marginal notes in the text. Claudin, Proctor and GW assign this book to the press of Pierre Levet, but BMC assigns it to Vérard, although among the "doubtful" books

GW 4969; HC 3690; BMC VIII, 96; Goff B-1053; Pell 2792; Claudin I, 437-8.

88 BOCCACCIO, GIOVANNI. Le Livre de la louange et vertu des nobles et cleres dames.

Paris, Antoine Vérard, 28 April 1493

Small folio (267 × 191 mm.). Gothic type (lettre bâtarde). 34 lines. [144] ff. (washed). 80 text woodcuts, including repeats (mostly approx. 90 × 80 mm.), but with a larger woodcut depicting a scribe at work on f. [3]v and another similar on f. [143]; large woodcut device of Vérard on last leaf. Dark red Jansenist morocco by Rivière; front doublure of one side of the original dark brown blind-stamped calf binding; g.e. Ms exlibris of François VIII de La Rochefoucauld (1673–1728) on title; from the libraries of the Château de La Roche-Guyon, with its small oval library stamp on first and penultimate leaves (its sale, Paris 1927, lot 14); of Boies Penrose II (sale, New York, Parke-Bernet, 28 Jan. 1947, lot 32), with his bookplate; of Silvain Brunschwig (his sale, Geneva, Rauch, 28 March 1955, lot 280), with his leather bookplate; and of Charles Van der Elst, with his leather bookplate.

First edition of the first French translation of *De claris mulieribus*, dedicated to Anne of Brittany by its anonymous author.

The book belonged to Francois VIII, duc de La Rochefoucauld and duc de La Roche-Guyon, grandson of Francois VI, the celebrated writer of the seventeenth century, author of the famous *Maxims*.

A curious feature of this copy is the offset impression on the (blank) verso of the last leaf of a work printed by Robert Estienne in 1535, *De transitu Hellenismi ad Christianismum* by Guillaume Budé. The impression is quite easy to read, implying that the printing must have been very recent when the sheets were laid down on top of the Boccaccio. The gap of more than forty years between the dates of the two volumes is hard to explain. Perhaps the Boccaccio stood in quires at the binder's and was bound up only as need arose; perhaps the binder put it, together with the Budé, in the press at the same time to prepare the two for binding for a customer, although since the Estienne title is not set straight on the last page of the Boccaccio, this seems unlikely. Most probably these and many other books were stored somewhere in sheets, either a binder's or a bookseller's warehouse, since we cannot trace any connection between Vérard and the Estiennes.

A fine copy of a handsome Vérard edition, with a very distinguished provenance.

GW 4490; HC 3337; BMC VIII, 79; Goff B-719; Pell 2478; IGI 1769; Morgan 504; Macfarlane 25; Fairfax Murray 50; LC/Rosenwald 418; not in Schäfer.

89 Hortus Sanitatis

89 HORTUS SANITATIS. – Ortus Sanitatis translate de latin en francois.

Paris, Antoine Vérard, [c. 1500]

Folio (290 × 202 mm.). Bâtarde type. 49–50 lines. 2 cols. 2 vols: CLXXV (i.e. 275), [16] ff.; CLXX, [27] ff. (lacking one blank leaf before the table in each volume, two worm punctures in second volume affecting a few letters, last 14 ff. of second volume – the tables – probably supplied from another copy). 4 full-page woodcuts (on versos of each volume title, of f. K$_5$, and of the section title of the final treatise on urine); 540 half-page column-wide woodcuts of plants, animals and precious stones; 3 woodcut titles in grotesque calligraphic style, numerous calligraphic woodcut initials with grotesque human faces throughout; woodcut printer's device on last page. Red jansenist morocco, gilt dentelles, gold-lettered title on spines, g.e. over marbling, by Chambolle-Duru. From the library of Marcel Jeanson, with his bookplate.

First French edition and the only complete translation of this lavishly illustrated guide to medicine for the layman, precious even at the time of its publication. The work gives an excellent idea of natural history in the period, and good examples of the widespread belief in fabulous beings.

The unnamed author is thought to be Johann Wonnecke of Kaub, physician of Frankfurt (ADB IV, 637), whose German original (*Gart der Gesundheit*, 1485) was enlarged and translated into Latin, probably by Peter von Viersen, professor of medicine at Mainz, first published by Meydenbach in 1491.

The illustrations are astonishing in their variety and beauty. According to Davies (Fairfax Murray Catalogue), many were copied from the second Latin edition (now generally assigned to Strassburg, Prüss, not after Oct. 1497). The full-page cut of the apothecary's shop on the section title verso of the treatise on urine is a specimen room, each jar labelled with the personal crest of the donor.

The full-page skeleton labels each of the bones in Latin. Preceding the section on birds is another large cut showing the author presenting his book to the king on horseback, with other persons engaged in falconry (II, f. 59). The large cut on the first title verso shows the author presenting his book to a saintly patron seated at a Gothic lectern, with four laymen looking on.

A beautiful copy of a rare book, no copy appearing on the market in over twenty-five years.

H 8958 (with erroneous collation); Goff H-490; BNIC H-297; Pell-Pol 5755; Pol 2004 (& Suppl.); IGI 4903; Klebs 509.5; Fairfax Murray 227; Macfarlane 140; Brunet III, 342 (with erroneous collation): "On trouve difficilement ces deux volumes réunis"; not in Schäfer.

90 [VALERIUS MAXIMUS.] – HESDIN, SIMON DE & GONES﹣
SE, NICOLAS DE, *trans.* Valere le grant.

Paris, Antoine Vérard, [c. 1500]

Folio (322 × 232 mm.). Bâtarde type. 50 lines. 2 cols. 2 parts in 1. [351] ff.
(of 352, lacking A₁ blank; small wormhole in inner margin in quires I and
K occasionally touching a letter; a little dust﹣soiling at fore edges at begin﹣
ning). With 9 large woodcuts, one at the commencement of each book;
plain black initials throughout. Contemporary, probably original brown
calf, blind﹣stamped in panel design with two different roll stamps (rebacked;
some repairs to both covers).

Fourth edition of the French translation begun by Simon de Hedin, a member
of the Order of St. John of Jerusalem, in 1375. He died while working on the
seventh book and the work was completed by Nicolas de Gonesse. This collec﹣
tion of moral historical anecdotes compiled during the reign of the emperor
Tiberius by Valerius Maximus was much read during the Renaissance for the
light it threw on the life and customs of Roman and Greek antiquity.

Vérard moved his business from the Pont Notre﹣Dame to "pres du carrefour
Saint Severin" in the latter part of 1499, but we do not know exactly how long
he was there; by 1503 he was again at a different address. The woodcuts are in
two different styles, and some consist of four smaller cuts grouped together.

This edition is very rare, there being no copy recorded in BMC, Goff, IGI or
Claudin.

Copinger 5932; Fairfax Murray 173; Macfarlane 153 (2 copies only).

91 BONAVENTURA (PSEUDO﹣). – QUENTIN, JOHANNES, *ed.*
Stimulus divini amoris devotissim[us].

Paris, Georg Mittelhus, 4 April 1493

Small 8vo (132 × 92 mm.). Gothic type. 26 lines. [136] ff., including the 2
final blanks (some dampstaining, occasional minor foxing). Guide letters.
Title inscription on bottom edges and a few marginal annotations in an
early hand. Old quarter vellum and boards covered with 16th﹣century
printed Latin leaf (stained).

A devotional treatise attributed to Saint Bonaventure on the title, but the
ascription of authorship is most probably due to its theme of submission to God
as a mystical path to knowledge, a theological concept propagated by Bonaven﹣
ture (1221–74), who argued for mystical illumination of divine grace against the
rationalist stance of Aristotelian theologians, such as Aquinas. General concensus
now holds against authenticity of authorship, and the work is cited under 'pseudo﹣
Bonaventura' in most of the modern standard bibliographies.

The printer of the present incunable, Georg Mittelhus, a German from Strassburg who was active at Paris from 1488 to 1500 (see Proctor II, 580-81 for the
discrepancy of Mittelhus' earliest dated Parisian edition), first printed the tract in
1490, as edited by Jean Quentin, a Doctor of Theology at Paris, but no recorded
edition includes any of Mittelhus' three devices. The type-faces used in the present
edition have been compared to those of Martin Flach of Strassburg and of Quentell. There are two known variants of the setting-up of the first two signatures;
the British Library copy contains the other.

GW 4823; HC 1131; BMC VIII. 126; Goff B-965; Pell 2662; On Mittelhus, see
Claudin II, 5-12.

AN ILLUSTRATED POETICAL INCUNABULUM
ONLY ONE COPY IN GOFF

92 SAINT-GELAIS, OCTAVIEN DE; LA VIGNE, ANDRE DE,
et al. Le vergier do[n]eur nouuellement[!] imprime a paris. De lentreprinse
& voyage de naples. Auquel est comprins comme[n]t le roy Charles huiti-
esme de ce no[m] a banyere desployee passa et rapassa de iournee en iournee
depuis. Lyon iusques a Napples. & de napples iusques a lyon. Ensemble
plusieurs austres choses . . . .

Paris, Jean Tréperel, c. 1500

4to (227 × 161 mm.). Bâtarde type. 45 lines. 2 cols. 182 ff. (few insignificant
mends, mostly in blank margins, tiny hole affecting outermost edge of historiated "L" on title). Half-page historiated woodcut initial "L" on title,
1 full-page and 14 large or small text woodcuts (3 repeated), Tréperel's
woodcut device on last page, several 6-line historiated woodcut initials, and
numerous 3-line woodcut initials. French 18th-century crimson morocco,
fillet border, back delicately gilt with flowers, leaves, and tiny stars, g.e.
From the libraries of Charles Butler (his sale, 1911, no. 1004); and of
Edouard Rahir (his sale, II, 1931, no. 308), with their bookplates.

A particularly attractive edition of an early French poetical miscellany which
appeared in several undated editions, not all of which are illustrated.

This copy is noteworthy for the address of the printer given on the penultimate
leaf - "la rue neufve nostre dame a lenseigne de lescu de France". This address
was unknown to Claudin and to the BMC and was apparently used by the
printer after his house on the Pont Neuf Notre Dame had been washed away by
the flooded Seine in October 1499.

Among the woodcut illustrations of the present edition, the bold historiated
"L" at the beginning is striking. There is also a full-page woodcut on the last
leaf of the author dictating his book which apparently has not been used else-
where. Nothing is known of the provencance of these or the remaining woodcuts,

except for the large cut of a bier (f. K₆v, repeated on M₂) which is copied from an undated Vérard edition of the *Jardin de Plaisance*, and the two cuts on f. FF₅ which are from an undated Vérard edition of *Therence en Francois* (see Macfarlane, pls. 40 and 42).

The text of the work is in two parts: the first is a long narrative, in prose and verse, of the French invasion of Italy under King Charles VIII in 1494; the second is a medley of various ballads, rondeaux, and acrostics, ending with a morality play on the last eight leaves. The work is usually listed under Octavien de Saint-Gelais (1468-1502), Bishop of Angoulême and uncle of the famous Mellin de St.-Gelais, merely because his name occurs first on the title; actually his contribution is limited to one poem (M₂-N₄). La Vigne was the author of the entire first part, of the morality play, and of several other pieces. There are at least thirty-four contributors to the book (see list in Rothschild cat. I, p. 290).

Not in Claudin, Fairfax Murray, Rothschild, Schäfer, BMC, IGI, Pol, IDL.

C 5993; Goff V-145 (one copy only); LC/Rosenwald 456; Tchemerzine (1977) V, 621 ("Edition rarissime"); Brunet V, 43-44.

93   Brocardica iuris

93 Modus legendi in utroq[ue] iure.

Paris, [Etienne Jehannot or Pierre le Dru], 24 September 1494

Small 8vo (140 × 94 mm.). Gothic types. 32 lines. [72] ff. (2 tiny worm-punctures in inner margin and 1 in fore margin). Full-page printer's mark on title, depicting St. Michael and St. James of Compostella supporting a shield with the three scallop shells of St. James, a sun and stars above; 5-line opening initial supplied in red and blue; smaller initials supplied in red or blue; paragraph marks in red or blue before headings; printed paragraph marks and capitals touched in pale yellow.

(*Bound with*:) Brocardica iuris.

[Paris, André Bocard, c. 1495]

Gothic types. 31 lines. [48] ff., including 3 blanks at end. Full-page printer's woodcut device with two angels holding a shield with the arms of France, below are the arms of the University of Paris and the City of Paris, the surrounding legend reads "Honneur Au Roy Et A La Court, Salut A l'Université Dont Notre Bien Procéde Et Sourt. Dieur Gart De Paris La Cyté." Paragraph marks supplied in red or blue before headings; printed paragraph marks and capitals touched in pale yellow.

(*Bound with*:) Flores legu[m].

[Paris, Jean Tréperel, c. 1498]

Gothic types. 24 lines. [80] ff. (title very slightly browned; small repairs to inner margin of b$_1$, affecting 1 letter of text, and fore margins of b$_7$ and $_8$). Full-page printer's woodcut device on title with angels holding the arms of France, below the initials I.T. held in a true-love knot by two lions rampant, surrounded by the legend "En Provocant Ta Grant Misèricorde Otroye Nous Charité Et Concorde"; 2-line initial supplied in red and blue; printed paragraph marks and capitals touched in pale yellow.

(*And with*:) LAURET, BERNARD. Casus in quib[us] iudex secularis potest manus in personas clericorum sine metu excom[m]unicationis impo-nere (and 4 other texts).

Paris, Antoine Denidel & Nicole de la Barre, [before 1497?]

Gothic types. 27 lines. [44] ff. Last page with printer's full-page woodcut device of Nicole de la Barre showing Adam and Eve holding a heart with the monogram NB and printer's mark, surrounded by legend "Benedicte Et Nolite Maledicere, Hec Dicit Dominus." Initials and paragraph marks supplied in red or blue, some capitals touched in pale yellow. Nineteenth-century jansenist olive morocco by C. Smith, gilt dentelles, g.e. Ms. exlibris on first title of the Congregation of Sts. Vanne (Vitonus) and Hidulf, the Abbey of St. Clement at Metz; 16th-century signature in red of Gerardinus Toussain, perhaps the rubricator? Twice on first title in an early hand "In te Jesu, spes mia recumbit", repeated on second title.

Four extremely rare legal incunabula.

Ad I: This edition of *Modus legendi* is recorded only in the Bibliothèque Nationale copy. It is an important key to the canonical and civil codes of law, naming their titles and contents together with their abbreviated forms. Victor Scholderer in a short article in *The Library* for April 1911, discovered an acrostic in the section beginning "Collige versus quid vult distinctio quevis" which attributed the work to one Werner von Schussenried, although, as he himself admits, numerous minor emendations are necessary to make it come out.

Ad II: The *Brocardica iuris* is an alphaebtical listing of citations relating to Roman and canonical law. All editions are known in only one or very few copies, and we have found no record of this one except for the present copy. GW cites it as being later than the fifteenth century, but the unworn state of the device suggests that it is pre-1500. All other instances of the device in this state are found in incunabular editions. Also, it does not occur in any of the volumes of Renouard-Moreau issued to date.

Ad III: The *Flores Legum* is a popular collection of verdicts and legal defini-tions written in proverbial form. Only 1 copy is recorded, cited by both Goff and GW.

Ad IV: The work by Lauret is one in which a determination is made on those cases in which a secular judge may order the detainment of ecclesiastics without fear of excommunication. Claudin knew of only the copy in the Maza-rine library and other than that there is 1 copy in the U.S. Concerning the date of this imprint, we know that association between Denidel and La Barre had ceased by 2 April 1497 when the latter had established himself in the rue de la Harpe and had changed his device.

This is an extraordinary sammelband of one unique and three remarkably rare legal texts, all complete and in fine condition.

Ad I: Recorded only in BNIC M-498; Renouard, *Marques typographiques*, 488

Ad II: No copy recorded; Renouard, *op. cit.*, 56

Ad III: GW 10062 (1 copy, Harvard Law); Goff F-216 (same copy); Renouard, *op. cit.*, 1074

Ad IV: C 3510 (but calling for only 41 ff.); Goff L-93 (1 copy, Huntington); BNIC L-68; Claudin II, pp. 263–64 (citing BN copy); Renouard, *op. cit.*, 526

94 BIBLE. LATIN.

[Lyon], Marcus Reinhart and Nicolaus Philippi, 1482

Small folio (271 × 191 mm.). Gothic type. 55 lines. 2 cols. (Interpretationes: 3 cols). [484] ff. (of 486, lacking initial and final blanks; restorations to inner margins of ff. 1, 8, 9, last leaf guarded; minor worming to first and last few leaves). First page with 14-line ornamental initial in blue, numerous other initials supplied in red or blue, the larger ones decorated, capitals touched in red, rubricated. At foot of f.g1 a paste-on with additional printed line. Printed side-notes in New Testament. Contemporary blind-stamped dark pigskin over bevelled wooden boards (rebacked, edges worn, clasps no longer present), panel design, center with intersecting fillets and fleurons. From the libraries of the Paris Church at Bingen (near Mainz), with its 16th-century ms. exlibris on first page and a presentation note (dated 1820) written by Leonard May, a parishioner, on front fly-leaf; and of the General Theological Seminary (NY) with its bookplate and embossed stamps.

The second Bible printed at Lyon and the third printed in France. It is one of the so-called "Fontibus ex Graecis Hebraeorum" editions, following Johann Amerbach's first of 1479 in providing a scholarly superior text (cf. distich at end of Apocalypse). Added are tables of Epistles and Gospels on six leaves and an index of Hebrew names ("Interpretationes hebraicorum nominum") on 33 leaves.

Reinhart of Strassburg, a kinsman of Johann Grüninger, and Philippi of Bensheim (Hesse) founded the second Lyon press in 1477 and continued their partnership until at least the end of 1482, the present production being the last to mention both their names in the colophon.

"Of the greatest rarity" (Copinger).

GW 4249; HC 3085; BMC VIII, 245; Goff B-574 (recording only two other copies); Pell 2311; Copinger, *Inc. Bibl.* 56.

ONLY COPY KNOWN: AN EARLY FRENCH POETICAL BESTIARY

95 DITZ JOYEUX DES OISEAUX, LES.

[Lyon, Printer of the Champion des Dames or Jean du Pré, c. 1485–1490]

Small 4to (193 × 135 mm.). Bâtarde type. 23–24 lines. 1 f., [8] pp., 1 blank f. = [6] ff. Large woodcut grotesque initial with 2 heads facing right, the neck of the upper grasped by the long snout of a fish; 2 pages with rubrication. Full red morocco, gilt dentelles, g.e., by Duru. From the libraries of Yemeniz (his sale, 9 May 1867, lot 1650), with his bookplate; of L. Potier (his sale, 29 March 1870, lot 793); of Henri Gallice; and Marcel Jeanson.

Unique copy of this French vernacular poem; apparently the first edition. The *Gesamtkatalog* locates only the present copy as do all other bibliographies.

The text consists of thirty-five quatrains, rhyming a-b-a-b, in which the birds offer moralizing instruction in their songs. According to the Rothschild catalogue, the work is "a symbolic composition derived from the *Bestiaries*, which were, as one knows, in vogue throughout the Middle Ages" (trans.).

The present book is one of a group of French-language poetry and prose texts issued without place, date or printer's name. Claudin called this anonymous press the "Printer of the *Champion des Dames*", from one of the books in these types, but the BMC gives convincing reasons for assigning all of the books in these types to the press of Jean du Pré, at Lyon. According to the BMC, the handsome large batarde type was apparently not used after August, 1490.

GW 8485; HC 1972; cf. BMC VIII, lvi, 280–282; Claudin IV, 414 reproducing grotesque initial; Thiébaud 281 (with erroneous collation).

FIRST EDITION OF A MAJOR ILLUSTRATED FIFTEENTH-CENTURY ROMANCE

96 FRANC (LE FRANC), MARTIN. Le champion des dames.

[Lyon, Jean Du Pré, before May 1488]

Small folio (258 × 192 mm.). Gothic type. 36 lines. 2 cols. [184] ff. (of 186, the two-line title supplied in excellent facsimile, lacking final blank leaf, last 3 ff. remargined, f. a8 strengthened at gutter, signatures x–z misbound between a and b, first 4 ff. with three worm punctures). 62 woodcuts, including 1 full-page (lightly foxed), 1 half-page, and the rest column-width. 19th-century calf antique, richly gold-tooled, interlacing strapwork design inlaid with variously colored leather, surrounding the gold-lettered title and a fictitious coat of arms, back with five raised bands (upper joint rubbed), gauffered and g.e., by Hagué. From the libraries of J. Renard (his sale, 21 March 1881, lot 517); of Baron Horace de Landau (his sale, 25 June 1948, lot 51); of Sylvain Brunschwig (his sale, 28 March 1955, lot 284); and of Albert Natural, with their bookplates.

First edition of a work of outstanding importance in the history of French literature and one of the major Lyonese illustrated books. It represents a defense of women against the accusations issuing from the authors of the *Roman de la Rose*. The two villains of the poem, Malebouche and Vilain-Penser, are believed to represent Guillaume Lorris and Jean de Meung. The poem praises the virtues of women in general and especially those of the House of Savoy.

The work provides a vivid chronicle of its time, describing the ills of a France torn by civil war and subject to English occupation. The author speaks of Pope

Joan and describes the courts of Artois and Picardie, mentioning numerous writers. A long passage on ff. 125ᵛ-126ʳ describes the music of the Burgundian court and names many of the composers who worked there. The author takes many viewpoints exceptional for his time: he exculpates Eve from blame for original sin, he views sorcery and witchcraft as the illusions of poor disturbed women, he describes Joan of Arc as animated by the Holy Spirit, unusual at a time when most writers spoke ill of her.

The author (c. 1395-1460), born in Arras, was secretary to the Duke of Savoy who became the anti-pope Felix V, and to Pope Nicolas V. Both of his extant works, the present one and *L'Estrif de la Fortune et de la Vertue*, were dedicated to Philippe le Bon, Duke of Burgundy, the great manuscript collector of the fifteenth century and the patron of many poets.

The *Champion* is the largest and most important of a group of over thirty works, all in French, all in the same types, and all apparently from the same press, identified by Victor Scholderer as the Lyon press of Jean du Pré. The beautiful woodcuts belong to the best productions of Lyonese masters.

A highly important incunable in one of the "famed" Hagué bindings.

HC 7311; BMC VIII, 284; Goff F-277; Pell 4892; Pol 2450; Claudin IV, 404-408; Rothschild I, 446; Fairfax Murray 171; Schäfer 131 (who, following GW manuscript, mistakenly lists the present copy as identical with the Florence BN copy); Brunet, suppl. I, 517 (citing this copy); Tchemerzine-Scheler III, 349-350.

96 Le champion des dames

**97 BREYDENBACH, BERNARD. – NICOLAS LE HUEN, *trans.*
La peregrination de outre mer en terre sai[n]cte.**

Lyon, Michel Topié & Jacques Heremberck, 28 November 1488

Folio (293 × 203 mm.). Lettre bâtarde. 38–39 lines. [132] ff., including first blank (lacking last 2 blanks; wormholes repaired in fore-margin of last two quires). 7 large folding copper-engraved plates (of which 3 are in excellent pencil facsimile – Venice, Rhodes and Methani; the 4 original plates are largely remargined and have small repairs, particularly in the folds; in two plates small holes are repaired and finished in pen facsimile). 1 full-page woodcut plate of animals, 6 small woodcuts showing costume and 6 small oriental alphabet cuts, each flanked by flower borders (some white on black); 1 large and 1 small representation of the Church of the Holy Sepulchre; large and small woodcut initials, all white on black ground. 19th-century French straight-grain red morocco by Koehler, panelled with four sets of double gilt rules, gilt dentelles, g.e.; in a morocco-edged box. From the library of M. N. Yemeniz (his sale, 1867, no. 2689).

The first edition of the first French translation, or rather, adaptation of Brey-denbach's voyage to Palestine in 1483-84. In 1487 Le Huen made a similar pilgrimage and used Breydenbach's book as a foundation for his own, changing dates, names, etc. where necessary and including a straight translation of Breyden-bach's journey to the monastery of St. Catherine, since he did not make this trip himself.

This is an important work in the field of graphic arts, since it constitutes the first use of metal engravings in a French book, comparable to Bettini's *Monte Santo* (1477) in Italy. These are all copies from the originals of Erhard Reuwich, who accompanied Breydenbach, and the large panoramas show a marked de-parture from the majority of fifteenth-century woodcut views, having an air of immediacy and authenticity from being taken on the spot, and showing much liveliness in the depiction of figures in various occupations. The most striking are the views of Venice and Jerusalem and the Holy Land. Also of great interest are the small woodcuts showing figures of Jews, Saracens, Turks, etc. in their native garb. These are based on the work of Reuwich, but are not stiff copies, having instead a fresh and lively feeling of their own.

This is a tall copy, larger than either the BM or Fairfax Murray copies, and in generally very good condition, apart from the small defects noted above.

GW 5080 (listing many incomplete copies); C 1337=3538; BMC VIII, 288; Goff B-1192; Pell 2982; Pol 898; IGI 2057; IDL 1027; Davies, *Breydenbach*, VIII; Fairfax Murray 624; Klebs 226.1; Claudin IV, 1–11.

98 OCKAM, GUILIELMUS DE. – [AUGUSTINUS DE RATIS-BONA.] Sup[er] quattuor libros s[ente]n[t]iaru[m] a[n]notat[i]o[n]es et ad ce[n]tilogii theologici . . . co[n]clusiones . . .

Lyon, Johannes Trechsel, 9–10 November 1495

Folio (278 × 194 mm.). Gothic type. 55 lines. 2 cols. [454] ff. (a few small worm-punctures at beginning and end affecting some letters, occasional light browning, some signatures misbound). Woodcut printer's device in red beneath colophon on f. x10, numerous 3- to 7-line initials and paragraph marks supplied in red and blue. Old calf-backed green marbled boards (rubbed), spine gilt, red morocco spine labels. Former owner's inscription and library stamps in blank portions of first two leaves.

First edition of Ockam's complete commentary on Peter Lombard's *Sententiae* (the edition of 1483 contained Book I only), a work which began as a series of lectures at Oxford (1312-13) to complete the formal requirements for his degree as *inceptor* or *baccalaureus formatus*. His new approach to philosophical inquiry in the work, which cast a critical eye on Duns Scotus as well as the philosophical tradition of scholasticism, incurred the suspicion of the papacy, and Ockam was summoned before the curia of Avignon to answer charges of heresy. Although never convicted, Ockam's Franciscan support of evangelical poverty and denial of the temporal power of the pope ultimately brought his excommunication, forcing him to seek the protection of the German emperor.

Ockam (c. 1285-1349) is considered the Father of nominalism, a philosophical system which claimed that abstract terms were merely names and had no real existence. It dominated the universities of northern Europe in the 14th and 15th centuries and played a powerful role in the shaping of the empiricist doctrines of Locke and Hume.

On the verso of the title is a letter from Badius to Trithemius emphasizing the importance of the work, reprinted in Renouard. The identification of the editor comes from Badius' dedicatory letter to Holkot's *Super Sententias*, 1497. At the end of the present edition is found the *commentatiuncula*, consisting of nineteen couplets in praise of Ockam, which form the acrostic: GUILHELMUM HUNC DE OCCAM IMPRESSIT TRECHSEL. The second text, the *Centilogium Theologicum,* consists of one hundred conclusions distinguishing empirical reasoning from doctrines of natural theology.

Complete copies of the *Sententiae,* possibly Ockam's most significant work, are quite scarce (several copies cited by Goff are incomplete). Ours, though some quires are misbound, is a complete, well-margined copy supplied with many large initials in red and blue and rubricated throughout (leaf ee8 and gathering ff misbound between cc7 and cc8; P bound in after R; X between AA and BB).

H 11942; BMC VIII, 297; Goff O-15; Pell-Pol 8630, 8631; Pol 2909; IGI 6956; IDL 3433; Renouard, *Badius,* II, 492-93; III, 90-92.

99 GUILLERMUS PARISIENSIS (i.e. JOHANN HEROLT). Postilla evangelio[rum] et epistolarum.

[Lyon, Pierre Mareshal & Barnabe Chaussard], 5 June 1497

Small 4to (91 × 128 mm.). Gothic type. 32–46 lines. 2 cols. [156] ff. (old pen trials, notes and ownership inscriptions on title, last page and endpapers). 16th-century limp vellum, raised bands (remboîtage).

A very rare edition of the popular compilation of Postilla on the New Testament, traditionally attributed to Guillaume d'Auvergne (d. 1249), but now thought to be the work of Johann Herolt, compiled in 1437. The compilation was made for members of the clergy seeking commentary on the lessons read at services throughout the year. The work filled such a great need that more than one hundred editions were published in the fifteenth century.

We have been able to trace only two copies of this edition, one in the Library of Congress, the other at Avignon. The printers Mareschal and Chaussard are classed among the dishonest printers of Lyons who plagiarized the prefaces of other publishers without citing them.

Goff G–702; Pell-Pol 5684; F. Goff, "The Postilla of Guillermus Parisiensis," *GJ* (1959), p. 78; not in Baudrier.

100 CICERO (PSEUDO-).– FRANCISCO MATURANZIO; ANTONIO MANCINELLI; FABIO VICTORINO, *comm.* M.T.C. Rhetoricorum Libri cu[m] tribus co[m]mentis.

[Lyon], Jacobino Suigo & Nicolaus de Benedictis, 13 May 1497

4to (250 × 172 mm.). Roman types. 47 lines of commentary. [278] ff. (F$_3$ signed E$_3$, M$_3$ signed M, and headline on E8^v upside down, as in BMC copy; small light brown stain in inner margin and dampstain in upper outer corner of first and last few leaves; 1 small worm-puncture in lower margin of last few quires, and larger worm-track in upper margin of last three leaves, no text affected). Decorative woodcut initials in three sizes, white on black. Contemporary wooden boards, crudely rebacked in old vellum; brass catches on three edges of lower cover (clasps lacking).

Generally a very nice copy of a rare edition of this pseudo-Cicero. The work is divided into two sections, the Rhetorica nova in four books and the Rhetorica vetus in two. It is reprinted from the first edition, Venice 1496, from which Mancinelli's mention of Antonius Moretus Brixiensis as the publisher (f. a$_2$) has been taken over unchanged.

Suigo and Benedictis were both from Turin and Suigo continued to be active there until 1497, but they printed together in Lyon up to March 1499, after which Benedictis carried on alone.

GW 6731; HC 5084; BMC VIII, 324; Goff C 684; Pell 3646; IGI 2973; Schweiger II, 114; not in Pol or IDL.

101 NINE WORTHIES. – Le triumphe des neuf preux . . . avec lystoire de Bertran de Guesclin. [Inc.:] Tresnoble et trescrestien charles viii. de ce nom . . .

Abbeville, Pierre Gérard, 30 May 1487

Small folio (271 × 197 mm.). Gothic type. 34 lines. [288] ff. (a few worm holes, mostly at beginning and end, occasionally affecting a letter). Large full page woodcut (188 × 133 mm.) on f. 1v and nine other cuts (c. 123 × 120 mm.); initials and paragraph marks supplied in red or blue throughout. 18th century speckled calf with the arms in gold of Julian Goldschmid on each cover, back elaborately gilt in compartments (rebacked, original back strip laid down); in a brown morocco pull off case by Zaehnsdorf. With ms. exlibris of Halge Demareste below the colophon; a coat of arms painted in the lower margin of f. A (azur, bande or, sur le tout trois roses gueules) is probably that of the original owner, but the arms have not been traced. (It is possibly a branch of the de Marets family, some of whom have three roses in their arms.) Armorial bookplate of the 18th century on f. AA; library stamp of the Bibliothèque Royale (France) on blank recto of f. AA; from the libraries of Julian Goldsmid (his sale, 11 Dec. 1815); Robert Lang (his sale, 17 Nov. 1828); Sir Thomas Phillipps, with later bookplate; and John Ehrman, with his bookplate and acquisition note.

A fine, complete copy of the third and last incunabulum printed at Abbeville. This is the first printed edition in French, with cuts probably made by Jean Dupré and here used for the first time. The large opening illustration shows an author presenting his book to the king; while the remaining illustrations of the nine worthies, – Joshua, David, Judas Maccabeus, Alexander, Hector, Julius Caesar, King Arthur, Charlemagne, Godfrey de Bouillon, and Bertrand de Guesclin – show each accompanied by his arms, within a thick black border. They are all in the conventional heroic style with the exception of Bertrand de Guesclin which appears to have been based on an authentic portrait.

Copies of this edition are rare and Goff locates only two in the U.S., one of which (P.M.L. copy) has the first and last leaves in facsimile. The present copy is a fine, crisp one with wide margins.

HC 15642; BMC VIII, 402; Goff T 458; Pol 3805; PML (Bennett) 623, with 2 illus.; Hind pp. 623–624, with 2 illus.

A DEVENTER INCUNABULUM

102 BONAVENTURA (PSEUDO-). Sermones quattuor novissimorum.

[Deventer, Richardus Pafraet, c. 1483–85]

Small 4to (191 × 136 mm.). Gothic type. 32 lines. [140] ff., including first blank (light soiling on recto of first blank). Spaces left for initials are filled by a contemporary hand with simple letters in ink. Modern brown morocco.

A rare Dutch incunable, Campbell knowing only of the copy at Deventer, and GW citing only nine copies in all. This copy is in fine condition.

Richardus Pafraet was the first printer at Deventer, and his first dated work was in 1477. Both he and his successor at Deventer, Jacobus de Breda, had two presses, and the close similarity of their types together with numerous unsigned, undated, books from each press has led to difficulty in assigning many of their productions. There is some disagreement over whether the present work should be attributed to the press of Richardus Pafraet or Jacobus de Breda, BMC opting for the former and GW the latter. However, a close examination of the type seems to indicate that BMC is correct, because the abbreviation for "us" here is that of 90G, and the round d with a flat head-stroke of that type is also present. In type 89G of de Breda, there are two additional forms of the "us" abbreviation and the round d has a curled head-stroke only. Recent scholarship by Lotte and Wytze Hellinga has also confirmed the assignment of this work to Pafraet's press.

The sermons are grouped around the subjects of Death, Judgement, Hell and Heaven, and the "Four Last Things." The first seven leaves contain an extensive table for the rubricator.

GW 4805; HC 56692; BMC IX, 46; Campbell 1336, Pol 3525 (Breda, 1480); IDL 971 (Pafraet, 1483–85); Hellinga, 15th-cent. Printing Types of Low Countries, I, 39–40; II, 499; not in Goff.

ONE OF THE EARLIEST BOOKS PRINTED AT ZWOLLE
SIGNED BY THE RUBRICATOR

103 BONAVENTURA, (PSEUDO-). Sermones de tempore simul et sanctis.

Zwolle, [Johannes de Vollenhoe or Pieter van Os], 1479

Small folio (266 × 204 mm.). Gothic type. 39 lines. 2 cols. [344] ff., includ-ing 4 blanks (blank lower margin of f. 10 restored; a few other neat marginal repairs, occasional minor stains). Initials supplied in red, paragraph marks and capitals touched in red. 18th-century light tan calf (light wear, joints starting), back elaborately gilt, covers gold-ruled, g.e. Rubricated 15th-century inscription on verso of blank first leaf "Liber mo[na]st[er]ii in Elze-chem (Elsegem) iuxta aldenardu[m] (Oudenaard) in Flandria" followed by the monogram TZ, repeated on ff. 2 and 342, the last in red.

First edition, first issue according to BMC, of one of the earliest books to be printed at Zwolle, and certainly the earliest substantial book. There are several undated works of 32 ff. or less including Bishop David of Burgundy's *Overijsel-sche Landbrief*, promulgated in June 1478 and therefore possibly printed in that year.

A fine crisp copy of a work long attributed to the popular Franciscan saint, and widely circulated under his name in the fifteenth and sixteenth centuries.

The last inscription and the rubrication of the first would indicate that "TZ" are the rubricator's initials.

GW 4810; HC 8976; BMC IX, 80; Goff B-948; Pell 2654; Pol 805; ICI 1939; Camp 336; IDL 968; see Hellinga, *Printing Types* I, pp. 40–41.

103   Exlibris followed by rubricator's initials

RARE INCUNABULAR COMPENDIUM OF SIX WORKS PRINTED AT LOUVAIN

104 BUTRIO, ANTONIUS DE. Speculum de confessione (with 5 other tracts, as follows:)

>   2. [JACOBUS DE GRUYTRODE.] Opusculum quod specu-lu[m] aureu[m] anime peccatricis inscribit[ur] incipit feliciter.
>   3. Tractatus artis bene moriendi perutilis.
>   4. HUGO DE SANCTO CHARO. Tractatus amantissimus qui speculum ecclesie inscribit[ur].
>   5. RODERICUS ZAMORENSIS. Speculum humane vite.
>   6. DIONYSIUS CARTUSIANUS. Speculum conversionis pec-catorum.

Louvain, Johann de Westphalia, [c. 1480]

Folio (283 × 205 mm.). Gothic type. 41 lines. 2 cols. [28; 16; 10; 8; 92; 16] ff. = [170] ff. including all 4 blanks (last work of 16 ff. apparently supplied from another copy; 2 ff. repaired in lower blank margin; very occasional minor thumbing). Large opening initial to each tract supplied in blue; other smaller initials supplied in red; paragraph marks, headings underlined, and capitals touched, in red (capitals of last tract touched in yellow). Con-temporary vellum over wooden boards (rebacked), small circular and hex-agonal blind stamps, 5 brass bosses each side, 4 brass corner reinforcements, 2 brass catches (clasps gone).

These six tracts comprise a treasury of mediaeval thought. Although the signatures run continuously, the fact that all the works begin on separate quires and have their own colophons and tables has inclined GW to suppose that these six *Specula* were intended to be sold individually. This conclusion is supported by the fact that the BMC copy is made up of some quires from the earlier (this one) of two undated editions by Johannes de Westphalia and some of the later (not before 1483). Complete copies are quite rare, Goff listing only 3.

Antonio de Butrio (1338-1408) was an Italian jurisconsult and a prolific author. Jacobus de Gruytrode (d. 1472), a native of Limbourg, was an ascetic prior at the Charterhouse of the Twelve Apostles near Liège. He was a very modest author and habitually attributed his own writings to the famous Dionysius Cartusianus of Louvain (d. 1471), whose work is represented here by the last tract. Hugues de Saint-Cher (d. 1263) of Vienne in the Dauphiné was the first cardinal from the Dominican order. Rodrigo Sanchez de Arévalo, Bishop of Zamora (1404-1470) was the Spanish prelate and noted author and diplomat.

GW 5829; C 1397; BMC IX 150; Goff B-1346; Camp 392; Pell 3126; Pol 947; IGI 735; IDL 1093.

105   ISIDORUS HISPALENSIS. De summo bono.

Louvain, Johann de Westphalia, 1486

8vo (183 × 132 mm.). Gothic type. 30 lines. [103] ff., including final blank [of 104, lacking first blank). 5-line opening initial supplied in blue, numer-ous 2-line initials supplied in red or blue; paragraph marks in red or blue, capitals touched in red heightened with silver. Vellum. Contemporary calligraphic exlibris inscription of Brother Gotfrid of the Dominican order, at the end of "Tabula".

Rare edition of Isidore of Seville's *De summo bono*, a manual of religion covering dogmatics, ethics, church law, asceticism, etc. In chapter 19, "De ecclesia et heresibus" he writes "Sancta ecclesia catholica sicut male viventes in se patienter tollerat, ita male credentes a se repellit. (The holy catholic church is patient with those who live badly, but rejects those who believe badly).

There were several editions of this work, but because of its immense popularity most are represented by very few copies. Of this Louvain edition there is only 1 copy in Goff.

Johannes de Westfalia was responsible for the introduction of printing to Belgium at Alost, where he set up shop with Thierry Martens, a native of that town. In 1474 he moved to Louvain whose first printer, Johann Veldener, had begun work earlier the same year.

HC 9285; BMC IX, 143; Goff I–194; Campbell 1023; Pell 6388; BNIC I–78; Pol 2145; IDL 2502.

105   Contemporary exlibris

106   BEETS, JOHANNES. Commentum super decem pr[ae]ceptis decalogi.

Louvain, Egidius van der Heerstraten, 19 April 1486

Small folio (280 × 206 mm.). Gothic type. 49-50 lines. 2 cols. [296] ff. (of 298, lacking the first and last blanks; first 20 ff. with light marginal damp-staining, one marginal tear repaired). First 18 ff. rubricated and initials supplied in red or blue; a few headlines added in brown or red ink. Light brown blind-tooled polished calf, antique (somewhat rubbed, upper joint starting). From the libraries of the Dukes of Arenberg with their characteristic label; and of Charles van der Elst, with his leather book-label.

Only edition of this work, very rarely found on the market. The present copy is among the first printed, as the words 'artis impressorie magistrum' in the colophon have been deleted in ink. These words were omitted in the second issue of this edition.

This commentary on the Ten Commandments is by Johannes Beets (d. 1476), a Carmelite friar who taught theology at the University of Cologne and Louvain, where he later became a member of the Academy and Professor of Holy Scripture. The *Commentum* is his only published work and it was never reprinted.

On f. 12 Jodoc Beyssel praises in a letter to his friend Arnold de Bost the quality of the work of Beets, mentions another publisher who was interested in publishing this book, and its hurried publication.

GW 3762; HC 2736; BMC IX, 165; Goff B-296; Camp 260; Pell 2018; Pol. 551A; IGI 1431.

COLARD MANSION LEAF WITH A LARGE WOODCUT

107 OVIDIUS NASO, PUBLIUS. – MANSION, COLARD, *trans.* and *ed.* Metamorphoses moralisés.

Bruges, Colard Mansion, May 1484

Folio (350 × 260 mm.). Bâtarde type, printed in red and black. 33 lines. 2 cols. One leaf (f. 69). Large woodcut (187 × 170 mm.); 2 initials supplied in red. Matted.

A magnificent leaf from the earliest and most sumptuous Flemish fifteenth-century woodcut book. No other book up to that time contained as large a woodcut as the present one. Deriving from Flemish miniatures in manuscripts now at Paris and Copenhagen (see Henkel), the woodcuts were the source of inspiration to Vérard's edition of 1493/4.

The present woodcut depicts *Phaeton before Apollo*, with the fall of Phaeton represented to the right through an arch. It marks the beginning of Book II.

As are all publications of Mansion, the 1484 Ovid is very rare; only twelve copies are known, at least five of them are incomplete, and only one of them is still in private hands. The complete book (389 ff.) contains seventeen large and sixteen small woodcuts. Mansion began his career as a scribe and illuminator, and as a printer became a pupil of William Caxton in Bruges, 1473-75. This Ovid apparently ruined him; he absconded from Bruges in 1484 and was heard of no more.

HC 12164; BMC IX, 134; Camp 1348; Pol 2955; Goff O-184 (3 incomplete copies); Duplessis, *Ovide*, no. 5; Hind II, 592; See M. D. Henkel, *De houtsneden van Mansion's Ovide moralisé* (1922); and J. Engels, *Etudes sur l'Ovide moralisé* (1945).

108 [LE FEVRE, RAOUL. – CAXTON, WILLIAM, *trans*. The re⁄
cuyell of the historyes of Troye.]

[Bruges, William Caxton, 1473 ?–1474]

Small folio (263 × 190 mm.). Gothic type (lettre bâtarde; Caxton type 1 throughout). 31 lines. [336] ff. (of 352; lacking 15 printed leaves and 1 blank, see below). Antique half morocco and wooden boards. Ms. exlibris of Matthew Forster, 1646, on first page; presented by him to Sion College; with its stamp on first and last pages and its engraved bookplate.

The first book produced by William Caxton, at his first press, and the first printed book in English. In its literary, cultural, and historical importance, it is one of the outstanding books of the fifteenth century.

Of the sixteen known copies, all except three are imperfect. The present copy lacks fifteen printed leaves, but has the very important ones with Caxton's colo⁄phons, the two leaves at the end of Book II (ff. 251–252), where Caxton originally intended to end his translation, and the one at the end of Book III (f. 351). In these, Caxton gives an account of his work as translator and printer. He ends Book II, "this said werke . . . was begonne in Brugis, & contynued in gaunt And finysshid in Coleyn . . . the yere of our lord a thousand four honderd lxxi". At the end of Book III he says, "Thus ende I this book whyche I have translated after myn Auctor as nyghe as god hath gyven me connyng . . . And for as moche as in the wrytyng of the same my penne is worn, myn hand wery and not stedfast, myn eyen dimmed with overmoche lokyng on the whit paper, and my corage not so prone and redy to laboure as hit hath ben . . . Therefore I have practysed & lerned at my grete charge and dispense to ordeyne this said book in prynte after the maner & forme as ye may here see, and is not wreton with penne and ynke as other bokes ben, to thende that every man may have them attones, ffor all the bookes of this storye named the recule of the historyes of troyes thus enpryntid as ye here see were begonne in oon day, and also fynysshid in oon day". This latter claim is, of course, a great exaggeration, but Caxton probably meant by "booke" simply a quire, or perhaps even just a page, which could easily have been run off in one day in all copies.

The title of this work does not give an adequate idea of its contents; it is a compendium of Greek mythology (Book I); a narrative of the life and deeds of Hercules (Book II); and the history of the siege and destruction of Troy (Book III). The style is that of a mediaeval romance grafted onto the classical plot.

The English language in Caxton's time was the speech of just one of the nations of Europe, and by no means the largest one. He himself, through his literary activity as a translator, as well as through his introduction of printing, was a key figure in the standardization of the language. His book stands at the head of the parade of literally millions of printings in English.

This book was printed without signature-marks or catchwords; it collates a–o10, p8; A–I10, K8, L6; AA–kk10 = 352 ff., the first being blank. Lacking in this copy are ff. a1–10; b1–3, 9–10; and kk10 = 16 ff. The last leaf had only some Latin verses on the destruction of Troy. Ff. [251] and [254] have been mended with some loss of text (about 40 letters per page). C. 50 leaves have been mended, some with minor loss or damage to the text. Upper portions of the leaves (top 8 lines) are dampstained. There has been no washing or pressing of leaves, however.

HC 7048; BMC IX, 129/130; Goff L–117; Campbell, 1st. Suppl., 1093a; Duff 242; STC 15375; Pforzheimer 594; de Ricci (C) 3.10; L. Hellinga, *Caxton in focus* (1982), pp. 83, 97–98; G. D. Painter, *William Caxton* (1977) for an account of Caxton's education as printer and beginnings of his press.

THE ROXBURGHE-SPENCER-DENT-HANROTT-ASHBURNHAM-BENNETT-MORGAN COPY

109   LE FEVRE, RAOUL. Le recueil des histoires de troyes.

[Bruges, William Caxton, c. 1474–75]

Small folio (267 × 196 mm.). Gothic type (lettre bâtarde). 31 lines. [252] ff. (of 286, lacking 32 printed leaves and 2 blanks: d–f10, C1, C10, and blanks a1 and m10). Early 19th-century brown straight-grained morocco, gold- and blind-ruled in geometrical patterns; gilt inner borders, g.e.; by Charles Lewis; in a morocco pull-off box. From the libraries of the Duke of Roxburghe (his sale, 1812, no. 6201); of the third Earl Spencer (*Spenceriana*, IV, no. 836; his duplicate sale, 5 June 1823, no. 120); of John Dent, with his notes (his sale, II, 1827, no. 1242); of P. A. Hanrott (his sale, III, 1834, no. 2063); of the Earl of Ashburnham (his sale, 1897, no. 2304); of Richard Bennett, with his bookplate; and of John Pierpont Morgan, with his bookplate and shelfmark.

First edition of the original French text, which appeared a little later than Caxton's English translation. This book may well be the earliest original literary work in French to appear in print. Caxton was already in England by early 1476. Printing in French at Paris began only in 1477, and the works in French printed by Le Roy at Lyon, in his first type-face, are all translations and most probably later, anyway.

Only seven copies of this book are extant, and only three of them are complete. This copy is especially notable for the fact that the first and last printed leaves are present, the missing leaves being all internal. It is in fine, unrestored condition throughout. It is also notable, of course, for its extraordinary provenance.

Le Fèvre's work was written for Philip the Good, Duke of Burgundy, and part of the book describes the foundation of the Burgundian dynasty by Hercules.

Philip himself formed one of the most dazzling collections of illuminated manu-scripts in all Europe, and it was his son Charles who married Margaret of York, Caxton's patron.

HC 7042; BMC IX, 131; Goff L-113; Campbell, 1st Suppl. 1093b; Duff 243; De Ricci (C) 3b.4; Pollard, *Cat . . . Early Printed Books . . . Morgan Library* (1907), no. 637 (this copy); L. Hellinga, *Caxton in focus* (1982), p. 83.

FROM THE FIRST PRESS IN BRUSSELS

110 CASSIANUS, JOHANNES. Collationes patrum XXIV.

[Brussels, Fratres vitae communis, c. 1476–1478]

Small folio (282 × 213 mm.). Gothic. 38 lines. 2 cols. [296] ff. (of 298; lacking first and last blanks; sewing-guards removed from center of each quire leaving light glue stain; minor worming in lower margin of quire [e] and part of [d]; lower blank margin of last text leaf renewed); uncut. Initials supplied in two sizes in red, paragraph marks and capitals touched in red; early vellum tabs. Old vellum. From the library of Charles van der Elst, with his leather bookplate.

First edition of the *Conferences* of Cassianus (c. 360-435), printed by the first press in Brussels. The author here recounts his conversations with the great leaders of Eastern monasticism. He spent much time in Egypt and Constan-tinople before establishing himself in western Europe where he founded two monasteries near Marseilles.

The Fratres Communis Vitae or Brethren of the Common Life was an association founded in the fourteenth century by G. de Groote of Utrecht to foster a higher level of Christian life and devotion. His followers laid great stress on teaching, founding schools all over the Netherlands and later in Germany, where an excellent education was offered without fees. To supply books for their schools, many of the members were engaged first in copying manuscripts, and then later in printing. The Brethren began printing at their house named Nazareth in Brussels in 1475 and continued for about ten years.

A fine, clean and unsophisticated copy of an important early example from the first Brussels press. No other copy can be traced in the postwar market.

GW 6159; HC 4561; BC IX, 173; Goff C-232; Camp 399; Pell 3339; Pol 1015; IDL 1159.

¶ Incipit prima collatio abbatis
ioseph de amicicia· Caplm primu

Beatus ioseph cu
ius nuc instituta
ac precepta pande
da sunt· vnus ex
tribus quorz in
prima collatione feam9 mcionem
dare admodu familie ac primati
us ciuitatis sue intra egiptu fuit·
q appellatur thmis· z ita non solu
egyptia sed eciam greca facundia di
ligenter edoctus· vt vel nobis vel
hiis qui eloquentiam egyptiam peni
tus ignorabant·non vt ceteri per
interprete ß per semetipsu elegan
tissime disputaret · Qui cu institu
tione suam nos desiderare sensiß·
paruclatus primu vtrui nam esse
mus germani fratres · audiensqz
a nobis q non carnali ß spirituali
essem9 fraternitate deiuncti·nosqz
ab exordio renunciationis nostre ta
in peregrinatione q ab vtroqz nos
tru fuerat obtentu milicie spiritua
lis accepta· qm in cenobij studio in
diuidua semp conuctione sociatos ·
tali vsus est sermonis exordio ·

¶Caplm secundu

Amiciciaru ac sodalitatis
multa sunt genera : que
diuersis modis humanu genus
dilectionis sodetate anectut Quos
dam eni precedens comendacio · pri
mu noticie · post eam amicicie feat
inire conuerca·in quibusda vero con
tractus quida · seu dati accepti vel

defectio· caritatis federa copulauit
Quos tu negociationis seu milicie
vel artis ac studij similitudo atqz
comunio·amiciciaru vinculis nexu
erunt · per qua ita eciam effera sibi
inuice corda mansuescut·vt eciam
hij qui in siluis ac montib9 latro
cinijs gaudent· z effusione huma
ni sanguinis delectantur· suorz sce
leru pticipes amplecctac ac foueat
Est eciam dilectionis z aliud gen9·
qd instinctu nature ipsius z consan
guinitatis lege anectitur· quo vel
contribules vel coniuges vel paren
tes seu fratres ac filij naturaliter
ceteris preferutur· quod non solu
humano generi· veru eciam omni
bus alitibus atqz animatibus in
esse dephendit·Nam pullos vel
catulos suos naturali affectu insti
gante sic ptegunt ac defendut·vt
frequeter p ipsis eciam obiecte se pe
riculis mortiqz non metuant·De
niqz eciam illa bestiaru vel serpentiu
vel alituu genera· q intolecabilis
feritas ac letale virus ab omnibz
separat et secernit· vt sunt basilisci
vel monocerotes vel gryphes· cu
eciam visu ipso cuiciis perniciosa esse
dicant·inter se tn p origine ipsi9
affectionisqz consortio·pacata z in
noxia perseuerat Sed hec omnia
que diximus genera caritatis·sicut
malis z bonis feris eciam atqz ser
pentibus videmus esse comunia:
ita eciam vsqz in fine certu est per
seuerare non posse·Etenim interru
pit ea frequeter ac diuidit locorz

III CARLERIUS, AEGIDIUS [OR GILLES CHARLIER]. Sporta fragmentorum. [*With*:] Sportula fragmentorum.

Brussels, Fratres Vitae Communis, 1478; 1479

Small folio (289 × 206 mm.). Gothic type. 38 lines. [281] ff., including blank f. 122 (but lacking final blank). One- and two-line initials and paragraph marks supplied in red; capitals touched in red; original manuscript signing and partial foliation; occasional marginalia. Antique dark brown calf over wooden boards (upper joint starting), gold-tooled and painted in a 16th-century white interlace design with blue and green cartouches, on a semé of blind and gold dots, frame of larger dots painted red, small oval sunk panel in center of upper cover with painted arms of Pope Leo X, a similar panel in lower cover with portrait of Saint Paul, arms of Leo X tooled in compartments on spine, light silver bosses of cherubs' heads, remains of metal clasps, edges gilt and gauffered with papal attributes, vellum endleaves, probably by Hagué-Coutin, Brussels c. 1885; in a black cloth box. From the libraries of Cardinal Giuseppe Renato Imperiali, with his red painted exlibris on a black background in lower margin of first leaf (see however below); offered in Olschki Catalogue 71 (1909), item 683; of Wilkins (his sale, Parke-Bernet, 29 January 1952, lot 86); and of Estelle Doheny, with her leather bookplate.

An early product of the first press in Brussels, and a fascinating survey of the moral and theological problems of late mediaeval France, in a splendid binding most likely by the famous Belgian forger Hagué-Coutin.

Thanks to the numerous monasteries situated in and around Brussels in the second half of the fifteenth century, the city was a center of book production, making it all the more astonishing that there was only one press working in the city, founded by the Brothers of the Common Life in 1475 probably with the help of Johann Veldener who supplied type. The press was primarily interested in liturgy and the Fathers of the Church, but also included more modern Christian authors.

Gilles Charlier (fl. 1431-1472) taught theology at Paris, and represented the chapter of Cambrai at the Council of Basel in 1432-1436. He distinguished himself at that council for his rebuttal to the followers of Jan Hus. In Cambrai he was widely consulted by clerics of his and neighboring dioceses. The present work provides his answers to questions in theology or discipline posed by his visitors. The view provided of late mediaeval morality is unusual in its scope, as he provides prescriptions or advice on incantations, attacks against the Virgin, communion under a single species, the ignorance of the Mendicant orders, celibacy, the sale of indulgences, the authority of the Pope, etc.

The master binder Louis (?) Hagué-Coutin (d. c.1890-91) worked for Zaehnsdorf in London in the mid-19th century, and did a good deal of work for Firmin-Didot. He was well known for his skill at recreating sixteenth-century bindings and his work appeared in several auctions. He later began to supply dealers with work which he did not identify as his own, and a renowned collection of his works was, through the agency of Quaritch, built up by one John Blacker who apparently believed them to be genuine early bindings. The Blacker collection was sold at Sotheby's 11 November 1897. By identifying works in that catalogue with items mentioned in Quaritch correspondence files, H. M. Nixon was able to enlarge the known number of Hagué forgeries. The present example is very similar to lot 91 in the sale, which also bore the arms of Pope Leo X, and is, as Sotheby's termed it "a very grand specimen of bibliopegistic art". In the 1950's it was still considered a genuine binding for Leo X and sold as such to Mrs. Doheny.

The Imperiali provenance may also have been created by Hagué, since this book neither appears in Fontanini's catalogue of Imperiali's library (1711) nor in the sale catalogue of 1793-1796.

GW 6136; HC 4513; BMC IX, 171; Goff C-200 (only 4 copies); Pell 3303; Pol 1011; IGI 2524; IDL 1153; see H. M. Nixon, "Binding Forgeries", *Lectures of the VIth International Congress of Bibliophiles: Vienna, 1969* (Vienna, 1971), pp. 69-81.

FINE FIFTEENTH-CENTURY DUTCH WOODCUTS

112   [LUDOLPHUS DE SAXONIA. Dat boeck va[n]den leuen ons liefs heeren ihesu cristi.]

Antwerp, Claes Leeu, 20 Nov. 1488

Small folio (269 × 196 mm.). Gothic type. 40 lines. 2 cols. 392 ff. (of 402, lacking first 10 leaves including title with woodcut; repairs to 13 leaves, mostly in blank margins, but in two cases touching the woodcuts) With 25 full-page and 119 half-page woodcuts, all with contemporary hand-coloring. Initials and paragraph marks supplied in red or blue; capitals touched in red or yellow. 18th-century dark brown calf, ruled in blind and stamped with a double border of intertwined ribbons and sheaves in 15th-century style (rebacked, original backstrip laid down); in a cloth box. Ms. exlibris of Jacques Peets (?), 1624 on f. nn₃; of Van Capenberghe, occurring twice on f. p₆, dated 1676, and on numerous other leaves throughout the book; of Paulus van Linthout, 1693, on f. y₁v; bookplate of C. W. Dyson Perrins (his sale, Sotheby's 5 Nov. 1946, no. 509); and of Charles van der Elst, with his bookplate.

One of the most beautiful Dutch woodcut books of the fifteenth century, showing a fascinating picture of the life of the period. These same cuts were used in the edition of Ludolphus' *Vita Christi* printed by Gerard Leeu in 1487 and some appeared earlier in the same printer's *Liden ons Heren*. These latter are vertical blocks with two architectural side-pieces added to make up the page width. According to Schretlen, these smaller cuts represent the work of the Gouda Woodcutter, employed by Leeu, and the twenty-five larger, full-page woodcuts are the work of his Antwerp Woodcutter. These two, were in turn based on the work of earlier Dutch woodcutters, which was copied by such artists as Israhel van Meckenem in his Small Passion series. In fact, these designs were copied so many times, with varying degrees of skill, that it is generally not possible to discover where they first appeared.

Ludolphus de Saxonia (d. c. 1370), a Dominican and then later a Carthusian, was the author in this Life of Christ of one of the most popular books of the late Middle Ages. There were numerous manuscript versions and over twenty printed editions before 1501.

Paulus van Linthout has written at the bottom of f. D3 in Dutch, "Pray for me, the blind sinner" and initialled it.

HC 10049 = H 10045 + 10050; BMC IX, 198; Goff L-355; Pol 2544; Campbell 1183; Schretlen, *Dutch & Flemish Woodcuts of the 15th c.*, pp. 31, 33, pl. 44, 45A and B, 46, 53, and 54C; Hind, pp. 566–70; Not in Schäfer.

A SPANISH INCUNABLE AND THREE POST-INCUNABLES

113 VERINO, MICHELE [i.e. MIGUEL VERI]. – SOBRARIAS, JUAN, *ed.* Liber distichorum.

Saragossa, [Jorge Coci & Leonardo Hutz], 1503

4to. Gothic type. 32 lines. [47] pp. (some light staining). Neat marginal and interlinear annotations by an early 17th-century owner.
(*Bound with:*) ALORA, JACOBUS, *ed.* Aurea expositio hymnorum.

Salamanca, Hans Gysser, 15 February 1501

Roman type for text and Gothic type for commentary. 34 lines (text), 54 lines (commentary). [44] ff. Woodcut royal arms on title (some spotting on title and some margins).
(*Bound with:*) SEDULIUS, CAELIUS. – SOBRARIAS, JUAN, *ed.* Paschale . . . cum additionibus sacraru[m] litteraru[m]: et indice auctorum in marginibus.

Saragossa, [Jorge Coci & Leonardo Hutz], [25 June] 1502

Gothic type. 23-31 lines. [114] pp., 1 blank leaf. Some ornamental woodcut initials. Title inscription (7 lines) and some neat marginal and interlinear annotations in two early hands.
(*And with:*) BASILIUS MAGNUS. – BRUNI, LEONARDO, *trans.* [De legendis libris gentilium] Magni Basilii perutiles de moribus institut[i]ones ad dulcissimos nepotes:quatenus humanitatis studiis imbuantur foeliciter incipiuntur.

Salamanca, [Printer of Nebrissensis 'Gramatica'], 1496

Roman type. 28 lines. [20] pp. (some stains). Marginal and interlinear annotation on first few leaves. Old limp vellum, remains of ties, ms. title on spine; endpapers from a printed "Rerum insignorum . . . Elenchus".

A fascinating collection of works reflecting the Spanish Renaissance and the effort of Christian humanists to reconcile Christian belief with the cultivation of Latin poetry and style. All four works are rare productions of early Spanish printers.

First are the celebrated distichs of the Minorcan poet Miguel Veri who died in 1487 at the age of eighteen. Written by an author famous for his simple style and pious life, and inspired by Greek and Latin philosophy, this work was printed many times in the sixteenth century and became a model of neo-latin

Fratris Didaci de Deça ordinis predicatoruz
uite regularis: Serenissimi ac magni hispaniaru
principis preceptoris. In defensiões sancti Lho
me ab impugnationibus magistri Nicholai ma
gistrieq Mathie ppugnatoris sui. Ad Illustrissi
mum ac Reuerendissimum dominum: dominum
petrum Mendoçe archipresulé Toletañ. hispa
nie totius primatem. sancte Romane ecclesie car
dinalem dignissimum. Epistola.

Llustrissimo ac Reueré

dissimo in cristo patri dño: do
mino petro Mendoçe archip
suli Toletañ. hispaniaq prima
ti: sancte Romane ecclesie car
dinali dignissimo. Frater Dida
cus de Deça ordinis predicato
ru uite regularis S. p. D. Non
satis cóstat pater optime an ue
ritas plures habeat sectatores an impugnatores
Et quidem ambiguú non est q a prima reru có
ditione: vix traxerit veritas sine aduersante mo
rulaz. ipsa teste veritate vbi de prima ac pulcher
rima inquit creaturarum. Ille homicida erat ab
initio ᴢ in veritate non stetit. Verum q alij sola
obsistunt ignorantia. Nam crebro: ut Seneca di
cit. mendacium specie ueritatis obcludit. Et si
cut tristem frontez amicus ᴢ blandam adulator
ostendit: sic uerisimilitudine ut uel fallat uel sur
ripiat: coloratur ueritas. hoc erroris exéplo ga
late deprehensi sunt: quibus Apostol' ait. O in

3

a ij

style. The present edition is by Juan Sobrarias (c. 1460-1528), a physician who became a professor of humanities at Saragossa.

Alora's commentary, with the text, of the most popular hymns of his time, was first printed in Seville in 1500. The commentary tries to present the hymns as just another form of latin poetry discussing the metre, the content and symbolism of each.

Caelius Sedulius (5th century) wrote the *Carmen Paschale* to demonstrate the extent to which Biblical history had mythological elements comparable to pagan mythology. His work also became a classic in the Middle Ages as a model of style.

St. Basil's work is a plea for Christian asceticism on the foundation of an hellenic education, citing Euripides, Pythagoras and Plato.

The first and last works are heavily annotated by two near contemporaries (possibly the owners of the book) and the ensemble provides a rich source for Spanish humanist studies in the Renaissance.

I: Norton 607; Palau 360399 (erroneous collation); not in Gallardo, Heredia or Salva.

II: Norton 523; not in Palau or NUC.

III: Norton 601 (erroneous collation); Palau 305732; not in NUC.

IV: GW 3714 citing only 3 copies; Goff B-277; Haebler (BI) 44; Vindel II, 107; Palau 290075; not in BM.

THE FIRST BOOK PRINTED BY UNGUT AND POLONUS

114 DEZA, DIDACUS DE. In defensio[n]es sancti Thome ab impugnati-onibus magistri Nicholai magistriq[ue] Mathie.

Seville, Meinardus Ungut & Stanislaus Polonus, 4 February 1491

Small 4to (175 × 125 mm.). Gothic type. 32 lines. [80] ff., including first and last blanks (headlines of 2 ff. shaved). Printer's woodcut device on last leaf. Dropside on first text-page printed in red. 19th-century Spanish tree sheep. From the libraries of the Dominicans at the royal convent of San Pablo, Cordoba, given by Fra Albertus de Sancta Maria (contemporary ms. inscription on colophon leaf); and of Estelle Doheny, with her leather bookplate.

First edition of the only Deza text printed in the fifteenth century and the first book (in a series of over 70) printed by the Ungut-Polonus partnership. It is a treatise in defence of St. Thomas Aquinas against the Biblical postils of Nicholas de Lyra and the replications of Matthias Doering, Franciscan provincial of Saxony. A very nice copy of a well-printed little book.

GW 8259; HCR 6040; BMC X, 37; Goff D-145; Pol 1242; IGI 3406; Vindel V, 71.19; Palau 71528 (mistakenly stating the text to be Spanish); Haebler 203 (also erroneously giving text as Spanish); Mendez-Hidalgo 87.22; Ruppel, *Polonus*, p. 19; Doheny Cat. II, 11.

he was a pylgrym of dux aas.

My lord the kyng sayd the foxe I pray you to retor
ne agayn I wil not that ye goo ony ferther with
me, ye myght haue harme therby, ye haue there two mor;
deuars arestyd/yf they escaped you . ye myght be hurt by
them I pray god kepe you fro mysauenture · wyth these
wordes he stode vp, on his afterfeet. And prayde alle the
beestys grete & smal that wolde be parteners of his pardon
that they shold praye for hym, They sayde that they alle
wolde remenbre hym , Thenne departed he fro the kynge
so skuply that many of them ermedy, Thenne saide he to
kywardꝰ the hare, and to bellyn th ramme merkly , dere
frendes shal we now departe/Ye wil and god will ac;
companye me ferther/ye two made me neuer angry/ye be
good for to walke wyth, courtoys/frendly and not com;
playned on of ony beeste ye be of good condicions ,and
goostly of your lyuyng/ye lyue bothe as I dyde/whan
I was a recluse,yf ye haue leeuis and gras ye be plesyd,
ye retche not of brede ,of flesshe /ne suche maner mete,
With suche flateryng wordes hath reynard thise two
flatred ,That they wente wyth hym tyl they camen to
fore his howes/maleperduys,

How kywart the hare was slayn by the foxe/cap°,xx°

Han the foxe was come to fore the gate of
his howes he sayde to bellyn the ramue /co;
syn ye shal abide here withoute/ I and kywart wille

115 Reynard the Fox (reduced)

❧ ENGLAND ❧

115 REYNARD THE FOX. – CAXTON, WILLIAM, *trans.* [Inc.:]
This is the table of the historye of reynart the foxe.

Westminster, William Caxton, 6 June 1481

Small folio (276 × 197 mm.). Gothic type (lettre bâtarde). 29 lines. [84] ff.
(of 85; the blank last leaf not present), including the inserted half-leaf after
f. h8 and the initial blank leaf. Initials and paragraph marks supplied in red.
Brown morocco, richly blind-stamped, in the style of an English 15th-
century binding, g.e. In a half-morocco drop-case. From the libraries of
J. Dunn Gardner (his sale, 1854, no. 461); of the Dukes of Newcastle
("Clumber" sale, 1937, no. 11); and of Martin Bodmer, with shelf-marks
and catalogue cards.

First edition in English, and as such, one of the earliest examples of prose
fiction in the language.

The story of Reynard is one of the great fictional themes. Its origin is apparently
French, from the 11th or 12th century, though some incidents go back to the
tenth-century *Ecbasis Captivi*, and even earlier, to the Aesopic fables of Indo-
European origin. Caxton's immediate source was a Flemish prose version, itself
derived from a verse version in the same language. As Caxton had resided for
years in the Rhineland and Netherlands, he was able to translate the *Histoire van
Reynaert de vos*, (Gouda, Gerard Leeu, 17 Aug. 1479). He speaks of his translation in the colophon, as follows: "For I have not added ne mynusshed but have
folowed as nyghe as I can my copye whiche was in dutche, and by me Willm
Caxton translated in to this rude & symple englyssh in thabbey of Westmestre.
fynysshed the vi daye of Juyn the yere of our lord .M.CCCC.Lxxxi. & the xxi
yere of the regne of kynge Edward the iiiith".

Unquestionably this is a "basic book" in world literature and in English
literature also, since Caxton was by far the most prolific translator of his century.
This translation of *Reynard* was perhaps his most popular, appearing in two
editions of his own, and about a dozen since then.

Blades, in his description of this work, assumes that the word "fynysshed" in the colophon quoted above applies to the translation and not to the printing, and in this he is followed by later bibliographers. It is difficult to understand this assumption as Caxton uses practically the same wording in the colophon of the *Descrypcyon of Englande*, 1480, where Blades assumes that it refers to the date of printing. The reason for the insertion of the half-leaf is doubtless a mistake of the original compositor who must have skipped a page of his copy and discovered the omission only after quire "i" was printed.

De Ricci records only five other copies of this work, three of them being less complete than the present one. This is the only copy in private hands, and only one other copy is held in the U.S. (Morgan Library). Our copy is in extraordinarily fine condition throughout. There is a very small mend to a corner of the blank leaf, and a few spots on some pages; occasional very neat interlinear Latin glosses.

HC 861; Duff 358; Goff R-137; De Ricci (C) 87.4; See also Blades, *Caxton*, 229–230.

THE FIRST ENGLISH ILLUSTRATED BOOK
THE FIRST SCIENTIFIC BOOK IN ENGLAND
THE FIRST ENGLISH PRINTED MAP

116 [GOSSUIN DE METZ. – CAXTON, WILLIAM, *trans*.] Mirrour of the world or thymage of the same.

[Westminster, William Caxton, 1481]

Small folio (275 × 210 mm.). Gothic type (lettre bâtarde). 29 lines. [96] ff. (of 100, lacking ff. b₁, k₁, k₈, and the blank a₁; tear in f. e₄ repaired; a few minor stains; last 3 ff. rehinged). With 11 text woodcuts and 25 (of 26) diagrams. Chapter initials and paragraph marks supplied in red. 18th-century English calf, ornamental gilt and blind borders. From the libraries of T. Skeffyngton, with his ms. exlibris on the first and third leaves; of R. Weller; (of Thomas Fuller, M.D., with his bookplate; see below); and of the Weller-Poley family, with their bookplate.

First edition in English of this mediaeval compendium of geography, cosmogony, meteorology, etc., and apparently the first work on physical science printed in the English language. It was traditionally ascribed to the encyclopaedist Vincent of Beauvais, but this is certainly incorrect; it is actually a translation, by Caxton, of a work by one Gossuin of Metz, which is extant in the original verse version as well as a briefer prose rendition; Caxton's translation is from the prose.

This is the first printed book in England to contain illustrations, comprising eleven woodcuts (c.70×90 mm.), as well as twenty-five woodcut diagrams (an additional diagram was on the missing leaf k₁). For some unknown reason, some of the diagrams had to be completed by handwritten additions, which are all in the same hand in all copies, and which many authorities believe to be that of Caxton.

Perhaps the most interesting of the woodcuts is the diagrammatic world map (f. e₄ᵛ) which is a modification of the traditional T-form; in this map, Asia, Europe and Africa are in the usual T arrangement, but are crowded into the northern hemisphere, the southern being designated "Inhabitabilis". On f. e₄ʳ we find the T-map in its usual state. Both are completed in ms. Other diagrams demonstrate the roundness of the earth, with men shown standing antipodally, and with small bits of land shown amid the oceans. Others show eclipses and other astronomical phenomena.

The illustrations display "schoolmaster" figures, such as the teachers of the liberal arts - the geometer, grammarian, logician, musician, etc.

This work is not entirely a translation, as there are lengthy additions by Caxton - a Prologue (3 pp.) and a postscript (1 p.) in which he gives an explanation of the genesis of his translation. It was made for Hugh Bryce, an Alderman of London, who wished to present it to William, Lord Hastings, Lord Chamberlain to Edward IV. The translation was made from a French ms. dated at Bruges, June 1464; Caxton began his translation on 2 January 1480 (1481 modern style) and finished it on March 8.

The T. Skeffington, whose ms. exlibris is on the first and third leaves of this copy, was probably the son of Sir William Skeffington (d. 1535), Lord Deputy of Ireland. The BL's copy of Caxton's *History of Jason* bears the same ms. exlibris. The Thomas Fuller armorial bookplate carries this added ms. notation: "He had this book bound and placed his Arms into it, in expectation of it being given to him by R. Weller"; evidently Fuller never owned the book, as the Weller-Poley bookplate is later.

HC 11656; Duff 401; Goff M-883; de R (C) 94 (this copy not recorded); Pforzheimer 1025; LC/Rosenwald 571; Klebs 531.1; BL, Caxton Exhibition (1977), no. 40.

THE ONLY COMPLETE COPY IN PRIVATE HANDS

117 CAXTON. – CHARTIER, ALAIN. – CAXTON, WILLIAM, *trans*. [Le curial. Inc.:] Here foloweth the copye of a lettre whyche maistre

Alayn Charetier wrote to hys brother, whyche desired to come dwelle in Court, in whyche he reherseth many myseryes & wretchydnesses therin used.

[Westminster, William Caxton, c. 1483]

Small folio (267 × 191 mm.). Gothic type. 38 lines. [6] ff. (somewhat foxed). Late 18th-century diced russia calf, panelled with double gilt rules. Ms. inscription (faded) on lower margin of f. 6ᵛ, Georgius Martinus (?) me iure vendicat; from the library of James Forbes (1749–1819), stating that he purchased it from Edwards in 1788; and of his grandson Charles (1810–1870), Comte de Montalembert, with their bookplates.

A very rare Caxton imprint, one of only three perfect copies, and one of the earliest known instances of printed English verse. Alain Chartier (c. 1392–c. 1430) was born at Bayeux. His brother Guillaume, to whom this letter was written, became bishop of Paris. Alain acted in the triple capacity of clerk, notary and financial secretary to Charles VII, and became vehement in his denunciations of the nobility and the clergy. The present work is a savage diatribe against life at Court and the courtiers of Charles VII – "For the courte is the nouryssher of peple whych by fraude and franchyse studye to drawe from one and other such wordes by whiche they may persecute them . . . and whyche take more playsir in false reportes than in verytable and trewe wordes".

Caxton says in the beginning that a copy of the French original was "delyverid to me by a noble and vertuous Erle" to be rendered into English, and it is generally believed that this Earl was none other than Anthony Rivers then lately beheaded at the order of Richard III. It would have been understood that Caxton's allusion was to his patron Rivers who had supplied him with the manuscript for his first production in Westminster, *Dictes and Sayengis of the Philosophers*.

At the end of this work Caxton makes one of his few ventures into verse, though without attempting the complex rhyming scheme of the original; the poem starts: "There ne is dangyer but of a vylayn/ Ne pride but of a poure man enryched/ Ne so sure a way as is the playn/ Ne socour but of a trewe frende."

This is the copy which de Ricci lists as having been offered for sale by Edwards as no. 565 in their catalogue of 1787. James Forbes' note on the flyleaf records his purchase of it from them for four guineas. His grandson Charles, issue of the marriage of his daughter Eliza to Marc René de Montalembert, was con-signed to his grandfather's care at the age of fifteen months. Below his acquisition note James Forbes has written an account of Caxton and the origins of English printing, taken from something called *A View of the State of Knowledge*.

De Ricci lists only 6 copies known, of which only two others are perfect (BM and PML), and one is a two-leaf fragment (Mellon).

GW 6563; H 4918; Goff C-429; STC 5057; Duff 84; De Ricci 20.5; Needham, *Printer & Pardoner*, CX58.

118 CHRISTINE DE PISAN. – WILLIAM CAXTON, *trans.* The book of fayttes of armes & of Chyvalrye.

[Westminster], William Caxton, 14 July 1489

Small folio (266 × 185 mm.). Gothic type (lettre bâtarde). 31 lines. [144] ff., including last blank (a few insignificant marginal mends). 19th-century English maroon morocco, gilt- and blind-ruled borders, corner ornaments, gilt back; g.e.; by Bedford. From the libraries of Magister Whalley (c. 1550), with his ms. library list on blank last leaf; of Francis Darwin, with his ms. exlibris (1884) and later notes on endpapers; of his son Col. Charles Darwin (1918); and of Martin Bodmer, with his shelf-marks.

First edition in English and the first English military book. It is a treatise on the laws of war, and military and naval strategy, based on Vegetius, Frontinus, and Honoré Bonet; the author must also, however, have used more recent sources as she describes the use of artillery and calculates the quantities of lead and powder needed for a fortress. The translation was made by Caxton at the request of Henry VII, from a French ms. owned by the King. The French original was printed for Vérard in 1488. Christine (1364-c. 1430) was a lady of the noble Venetian family of Pezano, whose father became astrologer royal to Charles V of France. She married Etienne du Castel, but following the deaths of her husband and her father, she turned to a literary career to support herself.

This fine and complete copy was owned by a Magister Whalley about 1550, judging from the publication dates of some books in his library list. This "Tabula Librorum Magistri Whalley" lists thirty-eight titles and includes both printed and manuscript works (mostly religious or legal, but also a few literary, e.g. *The collectyon of ye historyes of Troye* – no doubt Le Fèvre's *Recueil*). In many cases the citations do not give precise titles but rather content titles. Of the titles identifiable in STC, only two appeared in a single edition and can thus provide a *terminus post quem*: John Hall's *The proverbes of Salomon* (STC 12634. 1549?) and F. Bygod's *A treatise Concerning Impropriations of Benefyces* (STC 4240, 1535?). Magister Whalley may well have been Richard Whalley (1499-1583) who attended Cambridge (hence "Magister"), noted English politician, a partisan of the Reformation and an assistant to Thomas Cromwell and the Duke of Somerset. He was an ancestor of the Darwin family. The note in the hand of Francis Darwin (son of the famous scientist Charles Darwin) says that "this Book was found at the bottom of an old Elston hamper . . ." Elston was a long-standing possession of the Darwins, having been acquired by marriage in the seventeenth century.

Only four other perfect copies are recorded.

GW 6648; HC 4988 = 15918; Duff 96; Goff C-472; de R (C) 28 (this copy not recorded); Cockle, no. 1; Klebs 1022.1; STC 7269.

119 HIGDEN, RANULF. – TREVISA, JOHN DE, *trans.* Policronicon.

Westminster, Wynkyn de Worde, 13 April 1495

Small folio (250 × 188 mm.). Gothic type. 42 lines. 2 cols. [50], 346 (i.e. 347), [1] = 398 ff. including blank leaf hh₆ and the final leaf bearing only the Caxton–de Worde printer's mark (tear in first leaf repaired; corner of f. x₁ torn off with loss of few words, supplied in old ms; last 2ff. somewhat soiled; few minor mends; a few headlines slightly trimmed). 18th-century English red morocco (rebacked), g.e. From the libraries of Stephen Bateman; Robart Snow; and the Marquis of Northampton (see below).

The edition of *Policronicon,* or compilation of English chronicles, is notable for being the first English book to contain printed music notes (on f. 101). In Caxton's edition of this text (this being the second edition) a blank space was left for insertion of notes by hand. The text tells of the alleged discovery of the musical scale by Pythagoras.

Book I is a geographical description of the world; Chapt. 31, "On the islands of the Ocean" mentions a Wyntlandia, a possible reference to the Wineland of the Greenlanders who went to America c. 1000.

Ranulf Higden (d. 1364) was a monk of the Benedictine abbey of St. Werburg, Chester, and the author of grammatical and homiletic treatises also. His *Policronicon* was very popular in England for two centuries after its composition. It originally ended at 1327, but the present version continues to 1460. The large woodcut on the title (Hodnett 800) was made for the *Vitae Patrum* of St. Jerome published in the same year; it depicts a seated author, with a crowd of people standing before him.

On f. 182 is the very elegant ms. exlibris of Stephanus Bateman. It is dated April 29, 1568, records the cost of the book, and adds a quatrain embodying a splendid historiated calligraphic initial "W". Bateman (d. 1584) was a noted librarian and author who assembled the large library (6,700 volumes) of the scholarly Archbishop Matthew Parker (now at Corpus Christi, Cambridge). His best known work is *Batman uppon Bartholome,* 1582, a translation and revision of *De Proprietatibus Rerum* of Bartholomaeus Anglicus.

On f. 346 is the badly written exlibris of Robart Snow, above which is a scribbled inscription, apparently in Snow's hand, dated 1585. The volume was later owned by the Marquis of Northampton, whose Castle Ashby bookplate is on the front pastedown.

HC 8660; Duff 173; Goff H-268; Oates 4119.

120 [CHRONICLES OF ENGLAND.]

Westminster, Wynkyn de Worde, 1497

Small folio (260 × 183 mm.). Gothic type. 41 lines. 2 cols. [201] ff. (of 202;

lacking first leaf; tear in f. H₆ repaired; a few marginal repairs and a few worm-punctures towards end). With 4 woodcuts (one of them a repeat); a schematic cut (repeated 11 times); and the large Caxton–de Worde printer's mark at the end.

(*Bound with*:) HIGDEN, RANULF. The descrypcyon of Englonde.

Westminster, Wynkyn de Worde, 1498

Gothic type. 42 lines. 2 cols. [24] ff. (a few worm-punctures, some filled). With large woodcut on title. English 19th-century brown morocco, multi-ple gilt line. From the library of the Marquesses of Northampton, with engraved bookplate.

Ad I: A popular history of England, known also as "Brute's Chronicle", this text was written about 1460, and was first printed by Caxton in 1480. It is the first English historical work to be printed. It has been falsely ascribed to Caxton himself, and accordingly a pen "facsimile" replacing the missing first leaf is here lettered as "Caxton's Chronicle" on its recto (whereas the original is blank); the verso bears the beginning of the Tabula in ms. facsimile.

The colophon of this edition is notable for its mention of the St. Albans printer, this being the *only* extant information about him. It reads: "Here endyth this present cronycle of Englonde wyth the frute of tymes: compiled in a booke, & also enprynted by one somtyme scole mayster of saynt Albons, on whoos soule god have mercy, And newely in the yere of our lord god. M.CCCC.lxxxxvii. enpryntid at Westmestre by Wynkyn de Worde".

The woodcuts (Hodnett 886, 891) are imaginary views, one showing the building of the Tower of Babel; another, first entitled London, then Rome. There is also a depiction of Christ's Cross, and an often-repeated schematic cut.

The book seldom appears on the market; other than the present copy, none is listed in American auction records (1896 ff.) This is the most nearly complete one to have appeared in the records (lacking only one leaf).

Ad II: Higden's *Descrypcyon of Englonde* is an extract, somewhat rearranged, from Book I of his *Policronicon*. It was the first of that author's writings to appear in print, in 1480, before the *Policronicon* itself had appeared. The *Descrypcyon*, both in Caxton's 1480 edition and the present one (the only two incunabular editions) appears to have been sold separately as well as with the *Chronicles*, judging from its frequent appearance alone. Duff, Proctor and Oates all treat it as a separate work. The different datings of the two parts (1497 and 1498) would also indicate that the second work was to be sold separately. On the other hand, the *Descrypcyon* is mentioned at the end of the Tabula of the *Chronicles* (Aac^v), and Hain, GW and Goff therefore treat it as part f the *Chronicles*. The landscape woodcut on the title (Hodnett 1312) appeared only in this and one 16th-century edition of the *Descrypcyon*.

GW 6675: HC 4998; Goff C-482; Duff 102+104; Oates 4130; Pr 9707+9709; STC 9996+13440b.

121 ANDREAE, ANTONIUS. – THOMAS PENKETH. *ed.* Super XII libros Metaphisicae [Aristotelis] questiones.

[London], John Lettou for William Wilcock, 1480

Folio (278 × 197 mm.). 49 lines. 2 cols. [106] ff. including first blank (appearing here as the 9th leaf, because the eight-leaf "Tabula", usually found at the end of the book, is bound in at the beginning; some damp-marks throughout). English 19th-century dark blue morocco, blind-tooled, gilt. From the library of Sion College, with its engraved bookplate.

This is the first book from the press of John Lettou, London's first printer; he had previously printed a few broadsides in the same year. It is surmised that he was a native of Lithuania (from his name); and it is also surmised that he had been trained in Rome, since his first type is a font used by Johann Bulle of Bremen, who printed at Rome 1478-1479. Lettou printed only two books by himself (both for Wilcock), and then went into partnership with William de Machlinia, c. 1482, employing different types.

Antonius Andreae (d. 1320) was a follower of the scholastic philosopher Duns Scotus. His commentary on the Metaphysics of Artistotle was edited by the English scholar Thomas Penketh (d. 1487), noted for his profound knowledge of the Dunsian philosophy. He also dabbled in politics, being a devoted follower of Richard III, and an enthusiastic supporter of his deposition of Edward V.

William Wilcock, for whom this book was printed, was presumably a publisher, the first in England (as distinct from a publisher-printer, such as Caxton).

Only a few copies of this work are known, and the present copy is the only one in private hands. Other complete copies are at the British Library, Rosenbach Foundation (ex-York Minster), and the Morgan Library; two further copies, not known to be complete, are at Magdalen College and Dulwich; two incomplete copies are at Cambridge and John Rylands.

GW 1659; HC 976; Duff 26; Goff A-581; STC 581; Klebs 64.4; See also Duff, *Century of English Book Trade*, pp. 92, 97, 170.

THE FIRST ENGLISH STATUTE COLLECTION
THE LARGEST COPY RECORDED

122 [Abbreviamentum Statutorum.]

[London, John Lettou and William de Machlinia, c. 1482]

Folio (287 × 206 mm.). Gothic type. 40 lines. [108] ff. One initial in red and blue; numerous others in red; rubricated. Dark-stained wooden boards, calf back, antique style. Old ms. exlibris of Thomas Houdinge; and of Edward Combes on title and a few marginalia by Combes and others.

A fine wide-margined copy of the first edition of this collection of statutes in abridged form, in "Law French" and Latin. The statutes are alphabetically arranged, with an index on the first four leaves.

This is one of five undated books issued by the partnership of Lettou and Machlinia, the others being Littleton's *Tenures* and three year-books of Henry VI. Lettou and Machlinia were the first printer-publishers of law books in England, and this title is among the earliest such literature to have appeared. It is the first collected edition of English statutes.

There are eleven other copies recorded of this title. The present one is in unwashed condition and is the largest recorded.

GW 3; C 5609; Duff 375; Goff A-3; STC 9513.

123 Canterbury Tales

123   [CHAUCER, GEOFFREY. The Canterbury Tales.]
[London], Richard Pynson, [c. 1491–1492]

Folio (287 × 200 mm.). Gothic type. 33 lines (verse), 38–39 lines (prose). 1 col. (verse) or 2 cols. (prose). [311] ff. (of 324, lacking 12 printed leaves and 1 blank; see condition below). 34 text woodcuts (c. 85 × 114 mm.), including many repeats; printer's device at end. 19th-century brown morocco, inner gilt borders, gauffered gilt edges; by Charles Lewis for Richard Heber (1832); in a morocco pull-off case. From the libraries of William Herbert, the bibliographer; the Duke of Roxburghe (his sale, 1812, no. 3247); Richard Heber (his sale, IV, 1834, no. 817), with his acquisition and provenance notes; the Earl of Ashburnham (his sale, 1897, no. 1046); Richard Bennett, with his notes on front free endleaf; and John Pierpont Morgan, with his bookplate, shelf-mark and notes.

An important edition of *The Canterbury Tales*, "very probably the first book from Pynson's press" (Hodnett, p. 32). The woodcuts are derived from the set used in the Caxton edition of c. 1484, but with some added details, and they are generally considered to be more pleasing in appearance. "That they were engraved on the spot is clear from the fact that some were altered while the book was passing through the press and serve for different characters" (A.W. Pollard, *Cat. Early Printed Books . . . Morgan Library*, (1907), no. 750, this copy).

Richard Pynson was a Norman by birth and appears to have learnt printing at Rouen. His earliest dated book is November 1492, but at least five books were issued before that date. The type used here is a transitional *lettre de forme* or pointed gothic.

Many events in Chaucer's own life – his guardianship of two Kentish wards, his justiceship of the peace, his representation of the county in the Parliament of 1386, his commissionership of the river-bank between Greenwich and Wool-wich, all these contributed to his subsequent dramatic use of the crowds he saw on the Canterbury road. The pilgrims gathered in the inn at Southwark – the Knight, the Prioress, the Monk, the Pardoner, the Miller, the Merchant, etc., and, of course, the ever-famous Wife of Bath – were the product of his observa-tion and his imagination. He did not have to have read *The Decameron*, which we have no proof of his ever having seen, although some have said his work was based upon it.

The collation of a complete copy is: a-v^8 aa-kk^8 11^6 A-I^8 K^6 (last leaf blank). The well-documented provenance of this copy permits an interesting reconstruction of its ever-changing state of completeness: at the time of Herbert and Roxburghe it was lacking 57 text leaves (a$_1$, l$_2$, aa$_1$, C$_2$, and all after f. C$_8$). After Heber acquired it, he was able to supply all but ff. aa$_1$ and K$_5$ from another, shorter copy; he had these leaves expertly remargined and the book bound by Charles Lewis; the two missing leaves were supplied in excellent pen facsimile by Harris; one of them (f. K$_5$) is still present, as well as a genuine f. K$_5$ added some time before Morgan acquired the volume. When he purchased a second copy of the book, he had 11 leaves transferred from this copy (a$_{2-8}$, q$_4$, hh$_7$, D$_7$, G$_1$); all these, together with f. a$_1$ and the last blank (K$_6$) are still lacking today, f. q$_4$ is present in modern facsimile. Signature b was exchanged and is now a fraction larger than the subsequent signatures. 54 leaves are (still) remargined l($_2$, aa$_1$, C$_2$, D$_{1-6,8}$, E-F^8, G$_{2-8}$, H-I^8, K$_{1-5}$). FF, C$_8$ and K$_5$ are soiled and repaired, with loss of a few letters; ff. g$_{5-6}$, bb$_7$, gg$_8$, hh$_{3,8}$, and K$_3$ have minor marginal repairs.

GW 6587; HC 4923; Duff 89; Goff C-433; STC 5084; see also Hodnett, *English Woodcuts*, p. 32, nos. 1640–1668; Ames–Herbert–Dibdin, *Typographical Antiquities*, II, 21–525, with Herbert's remarks about his own (this) copy.

t   Her was in Aſie in a grete cyte
        Amonge criſten folke a Jurye
Suſteyned by a lorde of that countre
For foule vſure and lucre of velony
Hateful to criſt and to his company
And through this ſtrete men myght ryde and wend
For it was fre and open at euery ende
    A lytel ſcole of criſten folke there ſtode
Doun at the ferther ende in whiche ther were
Children an hepe comen of criſten blode
That lernyd in ſcole yere by yere
Suche maner doctryne as men vſen there
This is to ſay to ſynge and to rede
As ſmale children doon in theire childhede
    Amonge theſe children was a wydowes ſone
A lytel clergyon ſe vpn yere of age
That day by day to ſcole was his wone
And eke alſo where that he ſawe the ymage

124   GUIDO DE MONTE ROCHEN. Manipulus curatorum.

[London, Richard Pynson, 18 April, 1500

Small 8vo (119 × 85 mm.) Gothic type. 30 lines. 144 ff. Pynson device on title (third device, without border), (top outer corner of f. 4 burned away, affecting a few words of text, small hole below affecting two letters of text; fore margin of first signature trimmed narrower than remainder; some light staining at front and end of volume). 19th-century calf, blind-stamped (worn).

A rare edition of a work which appeared several times in the incunabular period. Of this edition Goff locates only the copy in the Pierpont Morgan Library in the U.S., while that in the British Library is described as imperfect. Written by a fourteenth-century Spanish theologian – a priest in Tereul, Aragon – the work is a manual on the sacraments for the instruction of priests.

Pynson printed two editions of the book in 1500, evidence of its usefulness and popularity, and this small "pocket" edition would have been a convenient size for a novice priest to carry.

Goff G-614 (the PML copy only); STC 12471; Duff 168; PML (Bennett) 759.

ONLY COMPLETE COPY KNOWN

125   GUIDO DE MONTE ROCHEN. Manipulus Curatoru[m].

Unassigned, 24 March 1497

Small 8vo (130 × 88 mm.). Gothic type. 32 lines. 145, [3] ff. (title very lightly soiled; waterstain in outer corners of lower margins of last three quires). Decorative woodcut initials, white on black. 19th-century vellum (small stain on front cover). A few lines of annotation. Ms. exlibris on verso of last leaf, H. Renoult, p[res]byter, Avranches, 1721.

Only one other copy is recorded of this edition of this little pocket manual for priests, and that copy lacks the title-leaf. There were several incunabular editions because undoubtedly every novice priest carried one in his pocket.

The type has a French look to it, but up till now has not been assigned to any one press.

IGI 4593 (Aosta); not recorded in any other incunabula bibliography.

126   La contenance de la table.

[Paris, Pierre Levet, c. 1490; i.e. Paris, c. 1850]

Small 4to (185 × 140 mm.). Gothic type. 17–18 lines. [6] ff. (uncut). Large woodcut initial "L" on title. 19th-century marbled boards with leather back.

A facsimile apparently originating from the hands of the notorious forger-restorer Pilinski, active in Paris in the second half of the nineteenth century. The type and text here seem to agree with Fairfax Murray 106. GW records only this latter copy and the one in the Chantilly Museum, noting a facsimile in Berlin.

The work is a curious and rather charming list of instructions to children relating to their table manners. It consists of forty quatrains and ends with a ballade and envoi. The opening lines are "Enfant qui veult estre courtois/Et a toutes gens agreable/Et principalement a table/Garde ces rigles en francois" and the poem ends with "Enfant prins ce tu est tenu/Des biens a qui te sont amasses/Dont ton estat est soustenu/Prier dieu pour les trespasses."

There are some half dozen incunabular editions, all known in very few copies.

Cf. GW 7449; Fairfax Murray 106; for text see A. de Montaiglon *Recueil de Poésies françoises des xv et xvi siècles*, I (1855), pp. 186–193.

An asterisk immediately before an entry indicates that this is a first edition.

INDEX OF TITLES AND AUTHORS

INDEX OF PRINTERS AND PUBLISHERS

INDEX OF SUBJECTS

INDEX OF PRINTING PLACES

INDEX OF PROVENANCES

PRINTED FOR H. P. KRAUS AT A. COLISH, INC., MOUNT
VERNON, NEW YORK. THE TYPE IS BRITISH MONOTYPE
POLIPHILUS. THE DESIGN IS BY KIT CURRIE
AND JERRY KELLY.